THE
WORLD EXPANDS

RECOLLECTIONS OF A ZOOLOGIST

George Howard Parker

STUDENTS and colleagues of George Howard Parker will find this book a confirmation of something long suspected, and other readers will make a pleasant discovery. The mind which evolved the complicated theory that chemical activation transmits messages from the nerve-endings to the peripheral organs is a mind of indescribable gentleness and wit. In an unhurried fashion Mr. Parker conducts the reader on a tour of memories. Teacher, lecturer, author, explorer — Mr. Parker might review the record of his contributions to science with pride and contentment, but these are the unassuming and recollections of a generous, delightful, and modest human being who will allow his stature to be revealed only inference.

THE WORLD EXPANDS

LONDON : GEOFFREY CUMBERLEGE
OXFORD UNIVERSITY PRESS

George Howard Parker

The World Expands

RECOLLECTIONS OF A ZOOLOGIST

By

GEORGE HOWARD PARKER, S.D.

Professor of Zoology, Emeritus

HARVARD UNIVERSITY

HARVARD UNIVERSITY PRESS

CAMBRIDGE · MASSACHUSETTS

1946

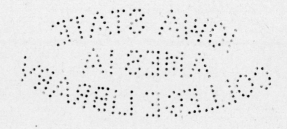

To

MY WIFE

WITH MORE THAN GRATITUDE

Preface

A little over a year ago, after I had completed what I had set out to do in a project on the coloration of animals, I resolved to undertake a new course of scientific work in this general field and while I was awaiting the arrival of the necessary material I began sketching, in a purely playful way, the following account of myself. As the exigencies of the war made it almost impossible for me to obtain what I needed for my new scientific venture, the free time thus thrown upon my hands led me to give more and more attention to this sketch of my life. Heretofore I had written only rather technical and detailed scientific papers and books. They had all called for close study and accurate record, and belonged to that kind of writing which is looked upon as dry. To attempt composition in a new field, such as that of autobiography, was to me a novel departure. To my surprise I found it unexpectedly entertaining. To recall and live over again the experiences of my past proved to be most exhilarating, and in this spirit I completed the early chapters of the present volume. Some of these were read by members of my family who encouraged me to think that I was not wasting my time. No one surely got so much enjoyment out of the effort as I did, for in writing these sketches I recalled a hundred other episodes that I thought about but did not write down, and thus I relived my life to myself with a fullness not represented in what is given in the following pages. Moreover, the composition was relatively easy as compared with that of writing scientific contributions. These required much outside reading and collation, whereas writing about myself was writing on a subject, the greater part of which was known to me without the pains of research. The ink flowed easily and the composition was of a kind which progressed with such freedom that I thoroughly enjoyed it. As the manuscript accumulated I began to wonder if in the end it might not be put into print. I therefore submitted about half of it, as much as had been finished at the time, to a friend, Mr. Byron S. Hollinshead, who had had much experience in passing judgment on manuscripts for the press, and requested him to give me an unbiased opinion on what had been written. He took great pains in the matter and finally returned an encouraging reply for which I was most grateful. This led me to resolve to finish the writing and to submit the manuscript when completed to a publisher. Thus an autobiographic account which had been began in a spirit of more or less playfulness became in the end a more serious project and resulted in the present composition.

It must be evident from what has just been said that I entered this novel occupation with no preconception as to the way in which an autobiography should be written. As a zoologist I had been prone to look upon man as one of the million or more kinds of animals already described by naturalists and as such to be subject to the same degree of study and consideration as any of his zoological associates. This does not mean that as a student of animals I had overlooked the extremely unique position occupied by the human species in the animal kingdom. Man differs from all other animals in the great diversity of his occupational opportunities. Whereas most animals by constitution live the life of a male or of a female of their kind and have almost no variety of occupation in each of these two categories, man is not only male or female, but may assume within each category one of hundreds of classes of social activities. He may be a tiller of the soil, or one of many kinds of artisans, a butcher, a baker, a candlestick maker, or he may enter the ranks of the professions as a lawyer, a physician, a clergyman, or a teacher, or any one of the thousands of other possible occupations. In this respect man has an outlook that no other creature approaches. From the zoological standpoint a human autobiography is a history of an individual in one of these innumerable vocational niches such as are made possible by our complicated social life. The following account of my days will be a portrayal of me as a student, investigator, and teacher in the scientific field of zoology with the view of showing its difficulties, its disappointments, its satisfactions, and its compensations and how they were met by a given human individual. The review is not a succession of confessions imaginary or otherwise, nor does it deal with fictions of other kinds. It is an account of the daily doings of a person whose aim it was to become conversant with animals including representatives of his own kind, and particularly with himself.

Contents

THE WORLD EXPANDS

I

Life Begins

I REMEMBER, I REMEMBER
THE HOUSE WHERE I WAS BORN
T. Hood

YOU ask me my name and I answer Howard Parker. At least so I was called by my family, my playmates, and my schoolteachers. My relatives said that as I grew to boyish maturity I begged for a part of my father's name, George Washington Parker, and I took a certain pride in the tradition that George Howard Parker, my mature name, was thus partly of my own choosing. This early adventure in selecting some of my own name was from time to time retold within my hearing, but it was not till many years later that I learned how completely misleading the whole recital was. In the spring of 1924 my intimate associate, Dr. William M. Wheeler, and I were planning a summer expedition to the tropical laboratory then being established on Barro Colorado Island in the Panama Canal by our good friend and colleague Dr. Thomas Barbour. At that time Wheeler and I were in Philadelphia for the annual meeting of the American Philosophical Society and we asked if in visiting the Canal Zone we needed passports. We were told that they were not necessary, but that a birth certificate might be found useful. As Philadelphia was my native place we went to the City Hall and for fifty cents I received from the Department of Public Health a duplicate of my certificate of birth carrying the name of our old family physician, Dr. Brooks, and stating that I had been born on the twenty-third day of December, 1864, with the name of George Howard Parker. Thus was my pride dashed to the ground and a half-century and more of family untruthfulness exposed to Bill Wheeler. He, loyal soul that he was, never "peached" on me or mine, but I from that day forth lost much of my confidence in what is commonly called the traditions of a family.

Dr. Brooks brought me into this world in a house now standing in Philadelphia at No. 114 Woodstock Street, a street which at the time of my birth was called Freelander Street. This is a small, secluded way leading from Race to Cherry Street and between Twentieth and Twenty-first streets. The whole neighborhood barely escaped extinction by the development of the Park Way which now stretches from City Hall to Fairmount Park. As you stand at the north end of the street on which I first saw the light and look down its length with Saint Clement's Episcopal Church appearing to close it off in the distance, the view is almost exactly that of my childhood days except that the cobblestones and the surface drainage of bygone times have given way to modern paving and a more hygienic system of water disposal. The street was a place of quiet and respected family dwellings and even under its new name it appears to have retained its early character to the present time. To have been born there might seem to be all that a modest Philadelphian could desire but, alas, even this bit of the town harbors a skeleton in a closet. That skeleton is the simple geographical fact that Freelander Street, the street of my birth, lies north of Market Street. And to those who are not conversant with the meaning of this statement let it be said that Market Street in Philadelphia is that east-west line south of which is all social sunshine and north of which is what shall we say? As a youth I was taught many of the habits of a correct Philadelphian, such for instance as walking always on the south side of Chestnut Street, but what was I to do about the place of my birth? Ay, there's the rub. For many years I have been a member of the American Philosophical Society, and when at its annual gatherings I enjoy its hospitality in the quiet setting of its ancient hall or when, in moments of relaxation, I wander with a congenial companion in the spring sunshine of Independence Square, I wonder if I have not by some irregularity slipped into that sunny part of Philadelphia to which my place of birth does not entitle me. I console myself, however, by recalling a generous remark once made to me by a good Catholic friend of mine who had been talking with me about the future, and who finally said that her Church knew full well that there were other ways of reaching Heaven than through the door of Rome.

My very early Philadelphia life was extremely precarious, for I was a sickly child. My mother once told me that during my first winter for a period of some three days it was not known whether I was dead or alive. Milk was the trouble, as it was in so many cases in those times, and it was not till the good Dr. Brooks suggested goat's milk that I took a turn for the better. From that hour on a nanny goat became a necessary adjunct to the household. Our maid of all work was a red-headed Hibernian, Mary by name, who once by accident allowed nanny to escape from our small garden. With a love for the open road and liberty, nanny took Horace Greeley's advice and went west into what then was more or less unoccupied territory. She was followed by Mary who, full of concern, shouted that if the goat was not caught, the baby would die. Near the Schuylkill she was corralled, a small boy paid for his services, and the baby in consequence saved. For a considerable time thereafter goat's milk formed a large part of my diet. That this ingredient saved me from an early grave I have no doubt. That it is responsible for a certain pugnaciousness in me, not evident, I must confess, in either my immediate maternal or paternal stocks, I do not believe. Nor do I admit that it has to do with a lifelong strong desire for food which has always characterized me. My mother once declared that I seemed to have been born one meal short and never to have caught up. I appear to be constituted as was Dr. Samuel Johnson, who evidently used his meals for measuring time, for he once observed that "He that sees before him to his third dinner, has a long prospect." In my mature life this strong natural appetite for food has been at times a great inconvenience, especially when it has failed to succumb to what is a reasonable supply of nutriment. This trouble is most likely to be with me at the seaside. Once at Woods Hole when I was describing an attack of this kind and what I had done to subdue it, including a retreat over a fence on the Main Street to a spot where in secret I ate one of Mrs. Eldridge's blueberry pies with more or less of the paper plate, one of my young listeners, Olga Osterhout, remarked in wholly untechnical language, "Why, Uncle Howard, you must have the hereditary of a goat." This comment was made without an inkling of the kind of milk on which I had been reared, or of the opinion held by my family that my infantile goat-milk diet had greatly increased my natural appetite.

But to return to my early life: naturally not much remains to me of this very vague era. My mother told me that she held me in

her arms when she and others went to watch Lincoln's funeral
procession as it passed through Philadelphia. This, if the account be
correct, was the nearest I ever came to the Great Emancipator.
History informs us that the date of the Lincoln ceremony was the
twenty-second of April, 1865, all of which marks me as a Civil War
baby. At that time my parents, my paternal grandparents, and I
lived together in the house on Freelander Street. The family was
one of simple and moderate tastes. Our table abounded in the best
from the Philadelphia farmers' markets, but not in costly exotics.
I can still recall the inviting breakfast flavor of Darlington scrap-
ple, and the coming in the spring of grass-butter. Yet with all this
wholesome living three generations of my immediate relatives had
never indulged in coffee. Tea we used, but coffee was not on the
household menu. Thus, in my youth, I had not even a vicarious
acquaintance with the Arabian berry. Strange as it may seem, my
familiarity with this beverage began when, as a university student,
I met it for the first time at a German pension in Leipzig. Nor
can much be said in favor of the coffee of this Saxon town in the
winter of 1891, for it was mostly chicory. But, however this may
be, I there and then acquired the habit of *Frühstück mit Kaffee*
and at least so far as the *Kaffee* is concerned the German indulgence
in the drink caught me for the rest of my days. I tolerated German
coffee as a necessity of the time and place, but as my European
wanderings carried me farther afield I made the acquaintance of
other brands. And at Naples in the late winter of 1893 coffee came
into its own. I immediately fell for the full-flavored, deeply roasted
caffè nero of Italy particularly as a demitasse after *collazione* or
pranzo. The taste was entirely different from that of the Teutonic
beverage; I was not obliged to acquire it: it was a gustatory love at
first sight. Whence this sudden and delightful acquisition, so Italian
in its way of conquest, at once delicious and evanescent yet virile
and lasting? Was I making up in one single draught for generations
of family abstemiousness? And then, after familiarity had paved
the way, the occasion of this almost insidious, caffeine magic suddenly dawned on me. As a very small child my mother had bought
me my first pair of shoes. I remember them well, for, as I was the
first-born in the family, the shoes were kept many years as me-
mentoes. Their uppers were delicate, black leather with white but-
tons, and their soles were very thin, tanned hide. Their toes, as I re-

call them in later years, were quite gone, as though nibbled away by a mouse, but not so! My elders said that the shoes were no sooner put on my baby feet than I drew one up to my mouth and began that process of demolition which eventually reduced the toes to nil. The taste of deliciously tanned baby's sole is almost exactly that of the best Italian *caffè nero*. This leathery fragrance had lain dormant in my nature a full score of years before it was finally reawakened in my growing maturity by the black coffee of old Nicolo's Neapolitan Trattoria. Long life, say I, to baby sole leather and to the *caffè nero* of Italy!

My parents, and in fact my whole family, were staunch Americans, or at least classed themselves as such. That meant in our region strong, almost I was about to say, devout Republicans. Hence it is a matter of no surprise when I declare that the first political slogan which I was taught was to shout, in my baby treble, for Grant and Colfax; as a result they were elected in 1868 to the presidency and vice-presidency of the restored Republic. This was the atmosphere in Freelander Street in those early post-bellum days. But it was not all political confusion and turmoil. It had its hour of quiet, and for me, even of inward repose. In the evening twilight after the day's activities were over, our family would often gather in the front parlor with the street windows open, and on favored nights the organ-grinder came. He was a sad-faced Italian who played over his repertoire of somber or lively tunes with the spirit, I am forced to say, of complete and absolute indifference. But not so I! I must detain him till he had come to my favorite piece, and to this end I wheedled from my father's pocket penny after penny which I then passed out the window hoping that the next would be my own piece. At last it would come—whereupon I would sit in what so far as I can remember was a child's sorrowful ecstasy, if such can be imagined. The mild emotion that possessed me was, as I recall, that pleasurable sadness such as brings grown-ups to pay the theater manager a high price for the privilege of shedding tears at what they call a thoroughly enjoyable performance. My emotional state still upon me, but the organ-grinder gone, I was carried off to bed. With changes in the season the Italian and his barrel-organ deserted Freelander Street, but a wish for my favorite music remained hidden in me. As I grew into boyhood my parents took me to matinees of one kind or another at the old Philadelphia Academy of Music, and on one memorable afternoon while I was listening with childish delight to an Italian opera, my long-lost, barrel organ music suddenly burst upon me. What a revelation! I had some vague idea that this music was the sole possession of my Italian and his music-box and lo! here it was filling with its sad melodiousness the whole of the great auditorium of the Academy. I was transported beyond words. It was the Miserere in Verdi's *Il Trovatore,* the soprano part of which was probably sung by Emma Thursby. Poor Verdi! Though he was not of the highest order as a composer, he could write music which charmed me as a four-year old and which continues to do so even in my old age. It was Verdi and his compatriot with the barrel-organ who gave me my beginner's course in what the academics call music appreciation, and from those days to the present, music has been my delight. Yet it has always remained to me an avocation with strong emphasis on the alpha privative, and in a way I am far from dissatisfied. Thus with Freelander Street and its associations my childhood came to a close, for when I was a little over five years of age we moved from the place of my birth to a much more commodious dwelling in a new portion of Philadelphia not far from Girard College. Here, strange as it may seem, the World began to open for me.

II

Education with a Capital E

THE FLAT TRANSGRESSION OF A SCHOOLBOY
W. Shakespeare

HAVING reached our new habitation in northern Philadelphia, my family resolved that I should be educated. Not that home influences had failed in their duties toward me, for I knew my letters, I could spell and read a little, and I had some knowledge of the multiplication table. My grandfather, who was a speaker at the orthodox Friends' Meeting, tried very strenuously to interest me in the Bible on Sundays. He would take me into the parlor and with great earnestness read to me from the New Testament. I listened, however, with indifference and continually steered him toward Noah and the Ark and Jonah and his Whale. Finally grandfather and I struck a bargain and agreed that the reading was to be divided partly of his choosing and partly of mine. I cannot say that the plan worked out well, but it relieved the family from the ignominy of having their first-born brought up in what some of my stiffer-necked relatives called a pagan life. The truth of the matter was, that we did not live near religious institutions which my parents approved of. They attended the First Unitarian Church under Dr. William Furness, then at Tenth and Locust streets, a long way off for a child like me, and my grandfather went far down Arch Street, nearly to Fourth Street, for his Friends' Meeting. The only public institutions that had any semblance of religiosity about them, and which were near enough to our new dwelling-place to be helpful to me, were the Eastern Penitentiary, the Sunday services of which were not open indiscriminately, and Girard College which Stephen Girard had so hedged roundabout with anti-religious rules, oral and printed, that the Bible and Ministers of the Gospel were not allowed under any circumstances to cross the threshold. It was said in our neighborhood that when a person of clerical cut made his appearance and applied for admission to the college grounds, he was never passed in by the gatekeeper till he was brought to the point of swearing. This was regarded by those concerned as a satisfactory test in conformity to the requirements of Stephen Girard's will and spoken directions. Under these circumstances, I was left religiously stranded, for on Sunday mornings all the older members of my family went their several ways, except grandmother who remained at home with me. She, I believe, was a Presbyterian as was my grandfather when he married her, his second wife. Grandmother never seemed to concern herself about her omission of a formal religious observance. We both stayed at home till the return of the others, I in play with imaginary companions behind grandmother's great chair and she, so far as I can remember, in quiet contemplation. In appearance she was almost a counterpart of Whistler's Mother, whose picture I never look upon without the vision of my grandmother seated in her chair in quiet thought. What passed through her mind during those placid Sunday mornings, I never inquired. My own occupation on the floor and behind her chair was a wonderful adventure with a fictitious playmate, Milkikokum by name; he lived with his family up a palm tree and spent his time killing lions and tigers on the beach, bringing their skins to his family in their platform house among the upper branches of the palm. At intervals in the Milkikokum drama, I would creep out from behind grandmother's chair and talk with her, though never on the subject of my unlettered playmate; it was on these occasions at the knee of this dear woman, and without the least suspicion of what was happening to me, that I absorbed more of the real truths of Christianity than I got from all else about me. Grandmother talked to me in the simplest words of everyday life, and I doubt if either of us ever appreciated the full import of what she was saying. It was, however, entirely appropriate to the time and place, though it was devoid of scriptural text and allusion. But the extreme informality of such instruction, religious or otherwise, did not appeal to my family, if indeed they thought of it as instruction at all, and so to school I must go. This decision was probably emphasized by the fact that a sister had been born into our midst and that I, as a five-year-old, even with a family helper to take part-care of me, was not to be put up with all day long at home.

So, early one morning, my hand in my father's, I was led to a small dames school in the neighborhood and arrangements were made for my instruction. The young woman who conducted this establishment of a dozen scholars or more inspected me with suspicion and asked father if I could spell. "Oh yes," said he with a touch of pride in his tone, "Howard has been taught at home." "Words of one syllable or two?" queried my future lady-mentor. "Two syllables," said Father. Then turning to me with deliberateness she said "Spell apple" to which I replied APPEL. With some severity she then declared "He may go in the one-syllable class." Father was chagrined, but I felt internally a mild resentment. Why should apple not be spelled as I had spelled it? I learned intuitively from this experience that according to the practice of correct orthography, apple should be spelled APPLE, but that to me spelled ap-ple and not ap-pel, all of which shows that I was born a reform-speller and there was an end of it. In fact I am so radical in this respect that even now I do not see why we should not spell the same word differently at different times, suiting the spellings to our momentary states of feeling. I certainly do this, and while my dear relatives call my attention to what they designate with a kind of superiority as failures in spelling, I retaliate by pointing out that my habit is Elizabethan, and that even so illustrious a person as William Shakespeare spelled his own name differently on different occasions. All of this was outmoded, I admit, when dictionary Johnson and his ilk came on the scene, but I am frank to confess that when this freedom in putting letters together as we wish was surrendered by us, a very picturesque feature of our language disappeared. It is true, however, that there are limits to such liberties, and though I am a great admirer of Benjamin Franklin for more reason than his advocacy of reformed orthography, I cannot go so far as he does in spelling our word wife YF. Yet by my family I am regarded as worse than a reform-speller. However, to myself I revert continually to a remark once made in my hearing by my revered teacher of English, Barrett Wendell, to the effect that if you write anything that is worth putting in type, the printing office will attend to your spelling, and if your composition is not worth printing, why bother? Still I cannot forget the advantage enjoyed by those in other language groups whose words are spelled as they are pronounced. German and Italian children, and perhaps still other linguistic units, never spend an hour in school in that futile task of learning to spell. They have no need of it. What a blessing the omission of orthography lessons would be in an American school, even where there are so-called good spellers! Why in adult life must we learn that our English cousins spell color with a U which we omit but that when they come to spell coloration they follow the American plan? Spelling in the English language is indeed a shocking abomination, and those of us who have inherited this tongue should never forget that an ounce of reform would be worth a pound of learning.

From the school of my parents' earliest choice, I was transferred to one nearer at hand and of greater gentility, for my family, as well as myself, was undergoing education. In the new school, which was kept by two very kindly sisters, we began the day by repeating a passage from the Bible, read to us in brief sections. We then turned to the three R's which kept us out of mischief for the rest of the morning, and shortly after noon we were sent home. We had, of course, a midmorning recess when boys and girls played together in a small, brick-paved garden. Here our budding preferences began to show themselves and I, a very blond youngster, chose in a very innocent way a striking brunette for my attentions. Why should my young sister, who was old enough then to be in the lowest class of the school, report this circumstance to the family circle? I believe I was described by the telltale informer as in love with a certain charmer. These were the first signs in me of the possibilities of matrimonial combinations, advantageous or otherwise, which fond parents pondered upon. The family evidently considered me with concern. Fortunately Freud had not yet appeared above the horizon or I might have been rushed off to one of his disciples for psychoanalysis. Nothing, however, was said to me, but I knew that the respective mothers held a confab, after which it was agreed to let matters take their own course. In a year or two my first affair had become history, but the experience had set me as a boy strongly in favor of brunettes, a response pattern which moves me still, even in full old age. Yet my own hair has gone from the extreme blond of my boyhood to a reasonably dark tone and is now drifting slowly toward white.

From this school of kindly and gentle influences, I was moved to the last institution for the instruction of youth that I was privileged to attend. This was a Quaker establishment known as Friends' Central School well in the heart of the city, as they say in Philadelphia, and fully two miles from our house. In this school boys and girls were separated, and I was subjected to a more masterful regime. I spent about five years at Friends' Central, two of which were in the lower school. Here I essayed my first English composition. The subject, after much deliberation at home, was the American Indian. To my great surprise, my composition was singled out to be read before the class, and the teacher's comment was to the effect that it was an unusually clear piece of writing. From that day to this my style in writing, if commented upon at all, has been described as clear. It is not picturesque, it is not poetic, it is not even interesting, but it is in general clear. Whence came this trait, for it seems to have been mine before I was trained in writing? In my first effort at composition the quality of a lifetime came into being, suddenly and without provocation. My belief is that my clarity in writing came from some deeper source than school, or any other type of training. And I am convinced that our educational systems can, at best, offer only a favorable environment in which the growing individual may expand.

As an educator I have often thought of this, and other like occurrences, with the result that I have concluded that many peculiarities which we show as our personal traits, favorable or unfavorable, are more frequently inborn than acquired. I know perfectly well that no single act of ours is purely inborn or purely acquired. The infant sneezes reflexly and with almost purely inborn capacity. As he grows older, he comes to sneeze either with the restraint of a politely trained person or with the explosive violence of a yokel. The sneeze is always there, but training or lack of training determines how it shall pass off. Even our heartbeat responds to the social environment and quickens to a friendly voice or slows to sad intelligence. We think we write our names in accordance with the way we have been taught, hence under the impress of our environment, but the signature of each one of us has an inborn trait which will identify that person the world over. I have often tried to evaluate that which we have by birth and that which we acquire from social contact, and I have concluded that we are perhaps about nine-tenths inborn and one-tenth acquired. In a measure this deflates the educator's balloon, but we must remember that what education gives us counts tremendously in everyday life, so much so that we certainly overestimate it in the balance of human totalities. What we get by education is a small acquisition planted on a very large inborn background.

Friends' Central proved to be a good school for me. Besides the ordinary English studies, we were schooled in Latin, in French or German, in drawing, in modern geography, and even in natural history. We also attended lectures on anatomy and physiology, physics and chemistry, subjects not commonly met with in the school curricula of those days. I recall that Friends' Central, probably because of these novel topics, had the reputation of not being a classical school. We did, however, read Caesar and Virgil, but there was no Greek. Our lectures on anatomy and physiology were given by a local physician who illustrated his remarks with a human skeleton and a sexless papier-mâché mannikin. The mannikin was a source of great horror to us all; in fact, one of the class fainted before this paper creature and was excused from the subject forever after. I can recall with what pleasure we escaped from under the eye of this wretched, painted dummy. Its realism had a disturbing emotional appeal to the class, and to me, though it was only a few years later, when I was some sixteen or seventeen years old, that I was delighted to help Dr. Henry Chapman dissect a young elephant recently deceased at the Philadelphia Zoological Garden.

Our lectures on physics and chemistry, illustrated by experiments, were given by one of the regular staff of Friends' Central School, Mason Child. These lectures were quite free from the disturbances attendant on anatomy and physiology and had an appeal to us of an altogether different kind. We took great pleasure in the experiments, particularly when they were accompanied by unexpected results, such as explosions. How delighted we were to see the burning of sodium on ice and how, after it had worked a hole into the frozen base, it exploded and sent droplets of burning metal straight to the forehead of our teacher. The class was dismissed and Mason, for in a Friends' School teachers were called by their given names, appeared the next day with a great white patch where the shot had taken effect. However, he taught us many things, or at least his experiments did. He was not so successful as a teacher in other sciences. We used Hooker's *Natural History* as a text in that subject, and among its many illustrations was a picture of a swallowtail butterfly; we were then collecting butterflies, as well as other insects, in Fairmount Park. The swallowtail in Hooker's book did not look like any of those which we had caught, and I was urged by the three or four in my class who were entomologically inclined to ask an explanation of Mason. He, innocent of what was in store for him, declared that there was only one kind of swallowtail, the one figured in our text. A few days later we confounded him with a box containing at least six different kinds of swallowtails, all of which had been collected by us, and asked him which was the butterfly shown in Hooker's book. He, poor man, was nonplused, and we beat a hasty retreat; he never returned to the subject. It was an example of not following Agassiz's advice: "Study nature not books." This was the rough and tumble of school life.

In Friends' Central we were all required to attend the midweek meeting, a morning religious service held in the large meetinghouse next the School on every Wednesday morning. Boys and girls in separate lines filed into the auditorium and took their places on the plain wooden benches, the girls on the right side of the hall and we on the left. The elders sat on raised seats against the far wall, facing us. At an appointed time all became silent and we remained in quiet meditation for what was supposed to be an hour. If any of the elders was moved to say anything, he or she rose and gave what might be called a very brief sermon or a prayer. A meeting might, however, be entirely silent. Woe be to any one of us whose favorite marble dropped out of his pocket and rolled with lengthy reverberations down the sloping floor till it struck with a sudden shock the foot of the platform on which the elders sat! So far as the culprit was concerned, nothing happened then, for the silence of the meeting was not to be disturbed, but, Oh my! Ordinarily, however, the meetings were not disturbed by mishaps of this or other kinds and we sat through our periods of meditation in relative quiet.

The senior member of the meeting on the men's side was Friend Longstreth, a very rigid and formal person. Across from him, and separated by a very narrow aisle, sat the first woman among the elders as the head of her section. In my day this was Lucretia Mott, who was then very elderly and frail but still fully alert. She often spoke in the meeting, with the same simplicity of approach which my grandmother had used, and she always gained our attention.

Not infrequently, after we had been sitting some three-quarters of an hour, she would rise and in a quiet but firm voice say that when she was a child she had found it trying to sit still so long, and that she thought the children had now undergone as much restraint as was good for them. She would then turn to Friend Longstreth and shake hands with him, a sign that the meeting was closed. Friend Longstreth with some unwillingness would acquiesce to Lucretia, for no one would have thought for a moment of opposing her wish, and we would then march out of the meetinghouse and back to our schoolrooms. I do not know whether Lucretia Mott understood all that she had done, for it was a rule in the school to add any time which was not used at meeting to our recess period, and we gained in this way many a quarter of an hour or less by the words of this dear woman. Her popularity with the school, however, rested not only on this generous thoughtfulness. Her brief talks to us on religious matters were all that could be asked for, and reflected the best that there was in Quakerism for a child. I was interested years later, on reading Hare's account of Lucretia Mott, to learn what these meetings meant to her. Hare remarks that it was her delight to come to "the midweekly meetings in Philadelphia which were attended by children from the Friends' Central School. She liked their fresh young faces and said they helped her to forget her own increasing feebleness and mitigate her loneliness." To feel that we thus contributed in some small measure to alleviate the infirmities of her old age is a gratifying thought to one who as a schoolchild sat in meeting near her.

In these respects Friends' Central was a notable spot for religious teaching, but I was not destined to graduate from the school, nor in fact to remain long in it. In the panic of 1877 my father's business met with complete collapse. Offices, house, and home were sold out and we were obliged to move to very restricted quarters, though still near Girard College, and to start at the bottom in earning our living. I shall not soon forget the day when Aaron Ivins, the principal of the boys' upper Friends' Central, called me to his desk, told me my school bill had not been paid, and escorted me with my few personal possessions to the door. It was a brief, sad, but final termination. Thus ended my formal school life for I turned now, at the age of about fifteen, to help support the family. I could not be said to be even partly prepared for the life I was obliged to take up, but necessity had knocked at the door and I had to abandon much that had been planned for me. In a sense the change was not without its benefits. I was thrown upon my own resources. My path in the immediate future was a rough one, but it was not without glimpses into what was to be for me, a wholly novel, strenuous, and exciting existence.

III

Boyhood Play

PARALLEL to my school life ran a life of outside adventure and sport, in which there was an ever-expanding view of the world ahead of me. To follow this stream of boyhood experience, I must transport myself back to the very early seventies.

We were then living in Philadelphia near the Eastern Penitentiary. The sidewalk near one long stretch of this institution was broad, smoothly paved with bricks, and slightly sloping. As this sidewalk did not abut upon private grounds, it was a famous course for mild sledding in winter and for velocipede riding at other times of the year. The velocipede, the forerunner of the bicycle, was then all the go. Some velocipedes were four-wheelers, others three. In my day the two-wheeler had not yet put in an appearance. Four-wheelers were usually in the hands of the small children; three-wheelers were reserved for the larger boys. I was a tall, gawky boy for my age and my parents, with an eye to economy, had provided me with a very large three-wheeler into which I was supposed to grow. Even with my rather long legs it was impossible for me to follow the full downstroke of the pedal, consequently driving my wheel was something of an acrobatic feat. However, I managed to do it and of course gradually outgrew my infirmity. The great sport with velocipedes was racing. Since there were a goodly number of us with wheels and as we assumed that we owned the Penitentiary sidewalk, the contests run off there were frequent and hot. One fairly large boy who had only a four-wheeler, which he had really outgrown but which he knew how to drive with great speed, challenged me to a race. My velocipede was of much greater capacity than his, but with my deficiency in leg length it was adjudged by those who looked on that it would be on the whole a fair race. The course was over a distance of half the block. At the start the four-wheeler took a good lead, but as my partial foot-shoves began to take effect I overhauled the smaller outfit and neck to neck we spun down the sidewalk. What happened nobody knew, but when we were at full heat something gave way and four-wheeler and three-wheeler became inextricably involved, one in the side gears of the other, and we fell in a confused tangle. Our friends extricated us and picked up our partly broken machines. Personally I came out whole, but my opponent met with disaster, for he had seriously hurt his wrist. We led him in tears across our street to his house, where he soon came under the doctor's care. His wrist was broken. The doctor did a poor job in setting it and my opponent never recovered the free use of the joint. After he got out, and for as long a time as I knew him, his wrist was stiff and he went under the cognomen of Corky. He was a real sport, however, and never blamed me for the mishap, but preferred to place it, as the Law so often does, amongst the acts of Providence. This indeed was the age of the velocipede and our accident was part of it.

A rarer sport than racing velocipedes, with the boys of our neighborhood, was skating. We lived near Fairmount Park and the Schuylkill, and in cold winters when the river froze over fully, skating on it was a great sport. As boys we were eager for the first firm ice. This did not form on the Schuylkill as soon as it did on the small ponds along the banks of that river. These shallow pools iced over relatively early, and though they were too limited in space for adult skaters they afforded my young associates and me the first taste of the winter's sport. We used these ponds before the ice on them was thick enough to be really safe, and one of our chief sports, slippery-bender by name, was to slide or skate across such ice accompanied by a crackling sound indicative of impending disaster. As each one passed over the thin ice successfully, he left it in a more dangerous condition for the next in turn.

Late one afternoon in early winter, we found in West Park close to the Girard Avenue Bridge an especially attractive pond. Most of it was well frozen and the skating there was good, but in one part of it the ice was thin and very inviting for a "bender." We would get a good headway by skating vigorously over the sound ice, and then in high hope literally fly over the weak area to reach firm ice on the

opposite side. What excitement as one by one we made the dash
with the "bender" ice cracking, and even bending in a wave, as we
shot across! Till, as ill luck would have it, I crashed in the midst
and went into the ice-cold water up to my middle. Fortunately the
pond was not deep and the firm ice was near, so I was soon out on the
frozen ground. But what a predicament! Wet to the skin over a
good half of my body, three miles from home on a cold winter
evening and without carfare! I was worse off than Tam o'Shanter
in his race for cover. However, I unlocked my skates and struck up
a lively pace over the Girard Avenue Bridge, through East Park
and the city streets toward home and warmth. As I ran or walked
my trousers, which were long ones, seemed to dry through. They
took on the firmness of stovepipes, with bends at the knees. I kept
up rapid locomotion and fortunately did not get chilled. I reached
home with a suspicion that I could pass it off without confession
to the family. Our house was provided with a large hallway register through which came an ample supply of warm air from the
furnace in the cellar. Over this register I resolved to put on the
finishing touches in drying before I presented myself to my parents.
I stood in the current of warm air some five minutes to discover,
however, that all I was doing was thawing out my trousers and
other frozen garments. Pond water was trickling from me in ever
increasing rivulets and running down the register and over the
floor. In this condition mother discovered me, took me to the bathroom, and in fact put me in the bathtub where I divested myself of
my wet clothing and, after a partial wash-up, put on dry apparel.
The family, of course, guessed what had happened and I was finally
led to a sheepish confession. No serious consequences followed. To
my companions and myself, it was a glorious adventure. We talked
it over later at school. No one even thought of the danger of
drowning, pneumonia, or even a cold. If it was not a part of the
day's work, it certainly was a part of the day's joy. It never even
dampened my ardor for "slippery bender."

But our most exciting game at this time was not racing velocipedes or even skating. It was playing Indians. Buffalo Bill, the Wild
West, and all such Indian headlines were then coming into their
own. Our game on these themes included cat hunting, climbing
trees, grape arbors, and fences, but above all building small fires
in the street on which our several habitations backed, and cooking

such food as we could procure. Next to the curb-stone of this back street we would start a fire of kindling wood from our parents' cellars, and after a good body of coals had formed roast Irish potatoes in the hot embers. How wild and woodsy was the taste of such semi-scorched or fully blackened morsels, especially in weather when there was a nip in the air! This fire episode was entirely contrary to city ordinances and was subject in consequence to raids by the police, all of which added to the fun of the game. I say police as though there was a whole force pitted against us, but this was far from true; there was only one officer allotted to our whole neighborhood and he, poor soul, doubtless had a very long beat. He nevertheless knew our ways and came upon us often just as the potatoes were reaching their best. He was a short, almost diminutive Irishman with a very large head. He was surely hydrocephalous. But his head was nothing compared to his hat which was so generous that as it spread over him, it gave him in totality the appearance of an animated mushroom. To us his name was Hunk-O'-Dee-Under-The-Hat. We never started one of our fires without posting a member of the tribe as a watch for Hunk-O'-Dee. Alarm would be given the moment he appeared at one or other end of the street and away we would scamper either into our gardens or houses or out of the street by its unprotected end. We would then slink back to some vantage outlook to see whether Hunk-O'-Dee had put out our fire. This he usually did, but I never knew him to take our food, not even a single Irish potato. His arrival marked the supreme height of our game and no Indian fire was a full success without a stealthy attack on the part of Hunk-O'-Dee-Under-The-Hat. I do not remember that my parents ever objected to the inroads which these games made on their woodpiles or their stores of potatoes. All families in our immediate vicinity where there were boys suffered alike and doubtless wrote the damage down to profit and loss.

At this time most of our neighbors were in relatively easy circumstances. To escape the excessive summer heat of Philadelphia my family, like many of those about us, formed the habit of making summer migrations to cooler regions. Our first extended outings of this kind were to Cape May, a seaside resort some hundred miles from Philadelphia and at the southernmost tip of New Jersey. Here we had pleasant and agreeable rooms in a cottage belonging to a small hotel conducted by a kindly Quaker, Mrs. Cooke by name.

The cottage in which we had our accommodations stood on an embankment within a few hundred feet of a wide, sandy beach on which broke the rollers of the open Atlantic. It was my first view of the ocean, and with the growing enthusiasm of a boy I could never see enough of it. To chase the waves, to dig for water in the sand, and above all to gather the clam and scallop shells, not to mention the big conchs and their long chains of egg-cases, these were the fascinations of the day. But perhaps best of all was to catch the little hermit crabs in their sea water pools and watch them pull back with lightning rapidity into their shells. Rarest of all was the brightly speckled lady crab with her sharp claws and sudden nip. To get her into my small bucket, aye, there was the trick! But my successes were my great secret.

My family was always among the earliest in the season to come to Mrs. Cooke's. My mother was especially pleased to settle herself in newly cleaned and freshly renovated quarters; hence our early arrival at the shore. Mrs. Cooke was kind enough to reserve for us the same rooms season after season so we really felt quite at home at her establishment. We had just made one of these migrations, when I was perhaps six or more years old, and after the usual unpacking had settled down to our seaside life when my mother became apprehensive of an unpleasant odor in our rooms. She called in Mrs. Cooke who at once recognized that something was wrong and at the suggestion of my mother had her man of all work go over the plumbing which our hostess had assured my mother had been put in the best of order before the season had opened. The man of all work made a full examination but could find nothing wrong. Then Mrs. Cooke, mother, and I started on a hunt. In my innocence I walked about with them till they opened a closet in our living room, on the bottom of which was my collection of shells from the beach and a few badly decomposed lady crabs. The surprise of the elders at this discovery was only equalled by their relief in finding the cause of the trouble. My malodorous seashore treasures were removed from the closet, the odor subsided, and the house was at peace. As I look back on this episode, I must admit that my mother was extremely lenient with me, in fact, I may say almost sympathetic, for she allowed me to keep the clam and scallop shells, all of which were clean and odorless, though the crabs and such things as had suffered a sea change into something rich and strange were no longer permitted. I continued, however, to collect many a shore oddity and by the time our vacation was over I had a large assortment of shells and pebbles, including some so-called Cape May diamonds, clear quartz pebbles as I afterwards learned. All these treasures I carried home with me, where they formed the nucleus of what was to be my natural history collection. These were my first efforts in zoology and allied sciences. Little did I then think that the study of such objects as samples of Nature's handiwork would become the passion of my life.

In the following winter my father, recognizing my growing interest in natural objects, took me to the Museum of the Philadelphia Academy of Natural Sciences where, for the first time, I looked on what was a professional collection of specimens of natural history. The collection was at that time housed in a building at the corner of Broad and Sansom streets, and as I recall it was dingy and poorly lighted. Nevertheless it was a source of great wonder to me that so much of the outside world could be brought together in bottles and under glass. I am sure I would have sympathized, after this visit to the Philadelphia museum, with President Lowell who in discussing our Harvard natural history displays, after having been appealed to by the Director for more building accommodations, remarked that such museums were evidently never complete till they contained one of every kind that was on the face of the globe. To me, the Philadelphia collection seemed to be exactly that. From my visit to it I carried away two very distinct ideas, one having to do with Embryology and the other with Zoological Systematics. From a case containing bottles of common mammalian embryos, such as sheep, swine, and the like, I inferred that animals started life in the bodies of their mothers as miniatures of their adult selves and that growth and maturing was nothing more than an expansion of this small form. I ranked myself at once as a member of the mistaken School of Preformationists, but there was time enough left me in which to learn better. The second lesson which I carried away from the Philadelphia museum was that every animal had, in addition to the common name that Adam was supposed to have given it, a technical designation of quite unintelligible but very learned terms. Having taken this in, I returned to my collection of shells at home with a feeling that I had really not done this full justice. To repair in a measure this neglect, I made my way to an assemblage of old schoolbooks in a storeroom on the top floor of our house and, having found a Greek grammar with a long list of terms meaningless to me, I proceeded to name my shells by writing under the crude sketches that I had made of them the designations alpha, beta, gamma, and so forth till I had provided each one with a *nomina parum intellecta*. Nor was I then satisfied in my endeavor to imitate the Philadelphia museum. I got possession of a large discarded kitchen clock with a glass door, removed its works, and built into it three or four wooden shelves on which I displayed my priceless specimens. Thus, at about the age of seven or eight, I began as the curator of a real though small museum, a position to which I was presumably self-appointed. My parents were not unmindful of my efforts and shortly after I had rebuilt the kitchen clock, I was presented on a certain Christmas with a small bookcase with glazed doors into which I moved my whole collection. This collection had, by this time, been extended from seashore shells to other natural objects, minerals, fossils, and in fact curios of all kinds; and I was fully established as the young proprietor of a growing museum.

IV

The World Expands

I SAW HIM RUN AFTER A GILDED BUTTERFLY
W. Shakespeare

HOW I was led as a boy of some ten years of age to Mrs. Helen S. Conant's book *The Butterfly Hunter* on the shelves of the Philadelphia Mercantile Library, I do not know. By some accident it came into my hands and its story of these winged creatures was opportune in more ways than one. It was a boy's butterfly annual. It began with the first of these insects to appear in the spring, the mourning-cloak butterfly, after which followed in natural procession the story of these gaudy creatures as they emerged one after another during the summer, till autumn when the last one in this gay parade crept into its winter hiding place to await the coming of a new spring. Told in simple language, the facts about butterflies as imparted in *The Butterfly Hunter* served as exactly the kind of introduction to whet my appetite for the hunt. Although the book was in conversational English, the reader was given the scientific names of the butterflies described and I came to know the mourning-cloak butterfly as *Vanessa antiopa* as well as under its vernacular. For several years at this time of my life, *The Butterfly Hunter* was my frequent consultant, for time and again I drew it from the Mercantile Library and carried it home with me for perusal. Swammerdam had his *Biblia Naturae* and I had my Bible of Butterflies.

It is a curious fact that almost fifty years after these occurrences, when I was walking on Chestnut Street, Philadelphia, with Dean Mead of Brown University, and we had arrived at Eleventh Street, I remarked "There stands the Mercantile Library Building where I found my first book in natural history, *The Butterfly Hunter*." On the spur of the moment we turned off on Eleventh Street, entered the library, and asked for the volume. The identical copy that I had used, much worn and dog-eared was put into my hands. The dean and I looked at it with interest, and I was about to return it to the custodian when my companion spoke up in my behalf and explained my connection with this particular copy. He then urged, rather to my embarrassment, that the volume, because of these early associations, be transferred to me. I finally could not resist. An exchange was arranged and *The Butterfly Hunter* original, if not perfect, now forms a part of my own library. From time to time I have enquired about the author, Mrs. H. S. Conant, but I have never been able to learn anything of her. I certainly owe her a real debt of gratitude.

In the early days in Philadelphia the butterfly fever was not only in my blood, but in that of several of my schoolmates. We formed a group who with nets, insect boxes, and ether bottles roamed the countryside about our native city. Saturdays, when there was no school, were our days for such outings. These expeditions extended from Philadelphia, as a center, in all directions for distances of ten miles or so. We took the Market Street or the Gloucester ferry to New Jersey where we found in its warm, sandy environment butterflies and other insects not common to Pennsylvania but belonging much farther south. Here we collected the rare Ajax swallowtail and the orange Terias, neither of them mentioned in our butterfly book. These discoveries brought us to the Philadelphia Academy of Natural Sciences where a wealth of volumes on our favorite insects were made available to us. Among these was the delightful volume by T. W. Harris on *Insects Injurious to Vegetation*.

On our return from expeditions into New Jersey we commonly crossed the Delaware River from Camden to Philadelphia on the Market Street Ferry and then took the Market Street car for home. From time to time we saw on the front seat of the open summer cars of those days a portly old gentleman who always sat near the driver and commonly talked with him. This elderly person was stout and full faced with a flowing, white beard not unlike the conventional Santa Claus. His appearance was such as to attract attention. As we left the car at Nineteenth Street, he continued on toward the Schuylkill and West Philadelphia. I asked my family if they knew who our elderly passenger could be, and they immediately declared that it must be Walt Whitman. They warned me to keep away from him, for he was reputed to be of bad habits. I could not imagine anything objectionable about a person whose appearance was so kindly, and yet I took the family advice and never sat on the front seat near him though my boyish inclination led me to be near the car horses at least. Thus, like Ulysses, I experienced but still escaped the magic of a siren atmosphere and lived to tell the tale. Years later, when I was stranded over a Sunday waiting for a through Boston and Maine train at Vergennes on Lake Champlain, I read at one session and for the first time *Leaves of Grass*. From that day on I understood both the danger and the majesty of Whitman. Since then I am prone to look back to my early and very distant acquaintance with this good, gray poet with a certain regret, and yet perhaps it was well that I kept my distance. His was too rich a diet for boyhood.

A great awakening in this period of my life was the coming of The Centennial Exposition to Philadelphia in 1876. This was held in West Fairmount Park, and was of unbelievable proportions for those days. The hundredth anniversary of the independence of our country could be held only in Philadelphia, for there our great Declaration was proclaimed on July 4, 1776. My father, like almost all other businessmen in Philadelphia, was involved in some part of the management of the Exposition. Hence he was able to get me a pass to the grounds while the buildings were under construction and the exhibits were being put in place. During 1875 and the early part of 1876, I spent many Saturdays watching the growth of the great show. The foreign buildings were a source of special interest to me and made world geography seem a real thing. I recall distinctly the construction of the Swedish building, and particularly the putting together of the Japanese house, a piece of work carried out by the first Orientals that I ever saw at day labor. From them I begged pieces of native Japanese wood, without doubt from their beautiful Cryptomeria forests, and I carried these treasured bits home to my collection of curios as souvenirs from the opposite side of the globe. As the exhibits were put in place, particularly in Machinery Hall and in the Main Building, I followed their growth step by step, so that when the Exposition was formally opened I knew almost all there was on show. From the enormous Corliss Engine to the small cakes of Fleischmann's dried yeast, nothing attracted me so much as the minerals in A. E. Foote's Mineral Exhibit. "See the Mineral World and Die" was his slogan, but before you die spend your last cent on specimens from A. E. Foote. And this I did, greatly to the apparent enrichment of my growing collection at home, but really to the replenishment of A. E. Foote's pocket. Amazon stone from Colorado and native sulphur from Sicily, what beautiful colors they had! These and many other purchases were carried to my cabinet and then put through blowpipe analysis according to Dana's Manual to show that they were what they were. All of which meant that I was becoming intensely interested in chemistry, a subject on which I was then hearing lectures once a week in Friends' Central School.

This, however, was only the preface to my new life. A particular schoolmate and I at this stage of our growth procured from Leary's Secondhand Book Store a copy of Steele's *Fourteen Weeks in Chemistry* and proceeded to spread it through a whole year of home experimentation. Finally, in what proved to be the culminating effort of our chemical exploits, we produced a light that really outshone Edison's best. We exhausted all our financial resources and bought from a chemical supply-house on Arch Street a glass bell jar, stoppered at the top and capable of holding some two to three gallons of gas. This, with great difficulty, we filled first with water and then, from a small retort, with oxygen gas. When all was ready, we invited the household into the room made completely dark by closing all the blinds and proceeded then to the illumination. A large-sized piece of stick phosphorus was put on a deflagrating spoon, touched off with a match, and quickly lowered into the jar of oxygen. The phosphorus burned with a tremendous evolution of light and in a moment the room was as bright as day. In fact it seemed to us that we had more than rivaled the sun. Not only did the phosphorus burn but also the copper deflagrating spoon, for an intense heat had been generated. Then as the family began to emit signs of wonder, the whole glass bell jar crumbled into a thousand fragments, crashed on the table, and allowed the suffocating fumes of burning phosphorus to permeate the place. Old and young, half choked with the white gas, plunged for the doors and sought free air. It was a marvelous triumph and a miraculous escape, but it ended further chemical exhibitions, for the family declined to advance money for the questionable pleasure of witnessing even the sun outdone.

We, however, quietly went on our chemical way, and having exhausted the inorganic part of the *Fourteen Weeks* turned to the organic part of this text. The first compound, the preparation of which was described, was picric acid. This we were told could be made by treating carbolic acid with a mixture of nitric and sulphuric acids. The inorganic acids we had, but carbolic acid was not on our shelves. Consequently, we invaded a friendly druggist's establishment and purchased a small phial of the carbolic ingredient. In the household storeroom, which was our improvised laboratory, we poured some of the carbolic acid into an evaporating dish and then added the mixture of the other two acids. Hardly had they met, when there was a terrific detonation and the evaporating dish, true to its name, completely disappeared, apparently reduced to atoms. My schoolmate set off the show and was therefore closer to the center of disturbance than I was. He was nearsighted and wore rather larger glasses, which was very providential, for after the explosion his face was marked with red points where small droplets of acid had hit him, his eyes fortunately having been protected by his glasses. I escaped with fewer marks, but I had my share. On recovery we looked at each other and asked what had happened. Later the druggist told us that he made up carbolic acid for sale by dissolving it in glycerine. It then dawned upon us that though we had doubtless made some picric acid, we had certainly also made some nitroglycerine which had fortunately destroyed the manufacturing plant before much of the product had been produced. Chemistry learned in this way is never forgotten, provided the investigator survives. As I remember we did not go farther with organic chemistry. We had had our fill! However, all this was of value to me, for in college I was noted for doing my laboratory exercises in chemistry with the least explosive violence.

But the world of minerals and of chemistry was not my only scientific interest. I had continued from my early days to collect insects, and now I widened my activities to other forms of animal life. My father would not allow me to use a gun, but a net was harmless and with this implement in hand I fished the ponds and streams in Fairmount Park, the Neck, the Wissahickon, and other parts of Philadelphia. Freshwater clams and snails, aquatic insects, sunfishes, young catfishes, frogs, tree toads, salamanders, snakes, and turtles all came my way and at home our garden threatened to change as le Jardin des Plantes in Paris had done from a botanical to a zoological park. My second sister was now some five years of age, and my elder sister about ten. These two girls were brought up in this medley of the animal kingdom and were accustomed to handle all my pets with freedom. From the very beginning and throughout their lives neither of them had any fear or solicitude in handling lowly creatures. They would pick up a gartersnake with as much impunity as they would a kitten, and stroke it and care for it with as much friendliness. The so-called inborn antipathy to lowly creatures, and particularly to snakes, supposed to be natural in man is in my opinion a pure myth. My sisters at least never showed it.

One of my interesting finds among insects was made in the Gorge of the Wissahickon. The side-streams that flow into Wissahickon Creek pour down through small ravines of their own making, cut through the gneiss rock of the region. This rock is full of small garnets roughly an eighth of an inch in diameter and nearly spherical. These crystals abound in great quantities in the beds of the Wissahickon's tributaries. Here the young of the caddis fly are very common, each worm-like larva living in its self-spun small cylindrical tube. One end of the tube is open, and through this the larva thrusts out its head and the front part of its body carrying the three pairs of legs. Thus the little creature, perhaps an inch long, can feed itself and scramble about in the water, carrying its tube with it. The end of the tube opposite the head is closed, and in Wassahickon caddis flies that end is always sealed with a single garnet, a truly imperial jewel as an emblem, but unfortunately at the tail of the little beast instead of on its head. The adequate resourcefulness of living nature is beyond belief!

In my endeavors to discover interesting creatures in the Philadelphia region, I occasionally brought home unwelcome acquisitions. One Saturday, after a day among the scrub pines of New Jersey, I returned with an improvised cloth bag containing a live black-snake some five feet long. This was rather more than the family could stand, and consequently on Sunday morning next I was dispatched with the snake to the Philadelphia Zoological Garden. Here my prize was received with pleasure and given a place in the Reptile House. My snake lived there in apparent happiness for a number of years. I had the pleasure of seeing my name among the donors to the Garden of specimens for the year, and of receiving a pass to the Garden good for a twelve-month. Thus I was gradually moving into the ranks of a budding zoologist when the financial calamity to my family, mentioned in an earlier chapter, brought much of this life of happy activity to a close.

V

Stern Reality

WHEN CHILL NOVEMBER'S SURLY BLAST
MADE FIELDS AND FOREST BARE.

R. Burns

WITH school behind me, I entered a world strange to me, in the
hope of gaining from it some form of livelihood. To find an occupation at once breadwinning and with some opportunity of educational advancement was not easy. One part of my family, with
kindly consideration of my immediate necessities, found a place for
me as a clerk in what was probably the best known of the retail
provision stores on Chestnut Street. My declination of this offer
offended them mortally I fear, but I had other projects in mind.
Although this refusal of mine relieved certain relatives of further
responsibility about me, it left me still on the street so to speak.
Many years later when my old friend Dr. Wheeler and I were attending a scientific meeting in Philadelphia we happened to be
passing the provision store whose early offer of work I had declined,
and in a moment of adventuresome freedom, I proposed that we go
in. At the counter we were met by a courteous clerk of much my
age who, after some conversation about his wares, sold me a small
box of fancy crackers of local and well-known manufacture. I
asked him how long he had been with the firm and he replied that
he had worked for them since he was a boy. I thanked him for the
crackers and Wheeler and I walked out of the store, whereupon I
remarked to Bill: "There I am as certain members of my family,
now all deceased, had destined me to be." Bill who knew the circumstances of my early life and who had entered into the spirit of
this Chestnut Street lark replied: "And if you had accepted the job
you might have led a much easier life than you have." Who can
tell? The quiet, courteous, gentle clerk, for such he was, looked as
a human being much better off than the overworked, fretted, and

worn-out professor. Bill and I both had a good laugh at the contrast.

But for me the streets of Philadelphia were a poor place to begin
picking up a living, for there were times when I lacked even such
rolls of bread as Benjamin Franklin once carried up Market Street
under his arms. My father had business associates in the publishing
house of J. B. Lippincott & Co. and through their consideration I
was enabled to act as a local sales agent for a new edition of Thack-
eray's novels which they were then publishing. It was my job to
obtain subscribers to the set of volumes and then, as one number
after another appeared, I would deliver them to the persons concerned and collect the price. My profits were not large, at most a
small fraction of a dollar a day, and though I completed the task,
I did not look upon it as promising. It helped, however, to keep the
wolf from the door. At brief intervals of freedom from my work
I had kept up my associations with the Philadelphia Academy of
Natural Sciences; here I learned, rather by accident than otherwise,
that there would soon be a vacancy in one of the two positions
under the Jessup Fund. The occupants of these positions were
known as Jessup beneficiaries, or less frequently as Jessup fellows.
Each beneficiary, appointed for a term of two years, received a
monthly stipend of twenty dollars, in return for which he worked
one half day in arranging some part of the Academy's collections
and the other half in any kind of natural history study that was to
his liking. The prospect seemed to me more than inviting and I
immediately applied for the position. I soon learned that I had a
competitor and that a member of the Academy's council, Dr. R. S.
Kenderdine, was appointed to examine us and to report his findings.
The examination was privately held for each candidate. It was oral
and rather searching. Shortly thereafter I was surprised and grati-
fied to learn that I had been accepted, though my opponent was
older and of wider experience than I. A year or so later when I had
come to know Dr. Kenderdine intimately, he told me that the
examination had been very close and that it had turned finally on
the replies we two had made to the same question. He asked my
opponent where his sternum was and he sheepishly designated the
seat of his trousers. When I came up for examination the same
question was put to me, and I replied that it was my breast bone.
This, the good doctor said, finally settled his mind in my favor. He

so reported to the council of the Academy and I was formally appointed to the place. Small as the stipend was, it could be relied upon, and in earning it, if I could be said to have earned it, I was working in a congenial atmosphere and at what I most wished to do.

Thus I became a part of the family at the Academy of Natural Sciences. My duties were to clean, order, and arrange the collection of butterflies, not a very large one, belonging to the institution and to help any visitor who might wish special information about insects. We had frequent calls from the lame Dr. Holt, who was Professor of Natural History in the Central High School, and from Dr. Hine, the newly appointed teacher of this subject at Girard College. I was warned in particular about one visitor who had perhaps the largest private collection of butterflies in the vicinity of Philadelphia and who came not infrequently to consult our collections. I was told that I must be sure to inspect the interior of his hat before he left our rooms, for he had been known to remove butterflies from collections not his own and to carry them off in his hat to where he thought they were more appropriately housed. This was a delicate task, but I accomplished it by the polite maneuver of taking his hat when he arrived, hanging it on a peg, and returning it to him when he went. Thus an apparently considerate formality covered my act as a detective, and I believe the Academy never lost an insect to this visitor during my two years of custodianship. These were some of my special duties as a Jessup Fellow, and their discharge in general was pleasurable rather than onerous.

As a member of the Academy's family, I was thrown with an interesting group of men. I was by far the youngest of them all, but I was invariably treated most kindly. I had entered the Academy in November 1880 shortly before my sixteenth birthday, and with the deficient schooling which I have described. In the Academy at that time were four former Jessup beneficiaries: Dr. Spencer Trotter, subsequently Professor of Natural History at Swarthmore College, Dr. Jacob Wortman, for many years Cope's chief collector in the western fossil fields, Dr. John A. Ryder, for a time naturalist to the United States Fish Commission, and finally Professor Angelo Heilprin, a geographer and paleontologist, later at Yale University, who died much too young. My mate on the Jessup Fund was Dr. Charles H. Townsend, for many years afterwards connected with the United States Bureau of Fisheries and subsequently Director of the New York Aquarium. The younger members of this group commonly brought their luncheons with them to the Academy. At the midday hour we retired to a basement room where we ate our repast around a table which served in several ways as our center of interest. At about this period two books had appeared that made a special appeal to young zoologists. One of these was Mivart's *Cat*, and the other was Flower's *Osteology of the Mammalia*. These books were eagerly read by us and kept within easy reach for reference. As a result of studying them we had all indulged freely in making skeletons—cats, turtles, dogs, birds, snakes, frogs, and even fishes, in part or as wholes fell into the boiling pot and came out clean bones. Many of these thus prepared, mostly as separate specimens, found their way into a large wooden box that stood by our lunch table. During the time of our repast it was usual for one of us to reach a hand into the bone-box, bring out as chance would have it a single bone and put it in the middle of the table for identification. Was it from a bird or from a mammal or from some other creature? If a vertebra, which face was front, which back, which above and which below? Woe be to him who did not know the law of the zygapophyses! Do prezygapophyses face upward or down? And so on through the luncheon which thus became food for the soul as well as for the body. The end of the meal was usually followed by a brief trip to the hall of the museum where a disputed point could be settled by reference to a mounted skeleton. By this kind of exercise we came to know bones as we did our alphabet.

When I went to Harvard I took a course in my second year on cat anatomy under Dr. Walter Faxon and in a joking way our instructor put a cat bone on a laboratory table, around which half a dozen of us had gathered, and asked what bone it was. The query was put to us in a challenging spirit. Most of the group gave up, but by the mere accident of my early training I felt at home with such a question. When the query was put to me I declared for the left navicular of the cat. We took the loose bone for final identification to a mounted cat skeleton and there the bone was in the cat's instep on the left side. Dr. Faxon looked at me in surprise, in fact he seemed almost appalled, till I told him of the training that I had been through. He then quickly saw that my kind of genius was all perspiration and no inspiration. Nevertheless, he was always thereafter more considerate of me and took a special interest in showing me the historical New England countryside in the neighborhood of Cambridge and Boston, for he was a born antiquarian.

Beside the younger men in the Academy's family, there were also scientific worthies of greater maturity but no less friendliness. The oldest of these was Titian Peale, whose artistic instincts led him to prepare beautiful illustrations of the American butterflies and moths which unfortunately never saw the light. Then there was the anatomist, Dr. Harrison Allen, a student of bats, who gave me my first lessons in anatomy by showing me how to dissect a snapping turtle. Of equal interest were the two notable students of American beetles, Dr. G. H. Horn and Dr. John L. LeConte, both much concerned with the collections of the American Entomological Society then stored in rooms at the Academy. We saw every week or so the Reverend H. C. McCook, who was at that time in the midst of his studies on the habits of American ants; and George W. Tryon, Jr., the curator of the Academy's collection of shells, was well started at this period on his colossal monograph of the shells of the world. These men and many others were among those who might be called the zoologically inclined members of the Academy's household, but beside them this institution found place for numerous botanists, geologists, mineralogists, and other natural historians whose total interests seemed to cover every aspect of Nature.

Perhaps possessed of wider interests than any of those already mentioned, and certainly most widely known of all in the world of Science, was Dr. Joseph Leidy. When I first came to the Academy, he was chairman of its board of curators and before I left that institution he had become its revered president. As Jessup students we came directly under Dr. Leidy's supervision. It was his habit to come to the Academy about once a week during daytime hours, and at such times we were always free to bring to him any difficulties that had arisen in our work. These matters he talked over with us with kindly consideration and interest. He knew us well enough to call us by our given names, which emphasized our apprentice to master relationship.

As I look back on those brief but not infrequent meetings with Dr. Leidy, I am impressed with what they really meant for me. Though a most distinguished scholar in the broad field of natural history, his remarks on any subject were in language so simple that anyone could understand, and though he often used technical terms he used them with a word of explanation which made them at once plain and clear. I have elsewhere described how he once spoke to a group of schoolchildren, on the form of the human skull; a strange subject to introduce to children, and yet he did it in such a direct and simple manner that in a few minutes he had all the youngsters fully aroused and eager to grasp all that he described to them. His talk was especially instructive to me, as I listened from the outskirts of the group, to see how he used technical terms. He remarked when he came to the foramen magnum that this was the largest opening in the skull and that it was the aperture for the connection between the brain and the spinal cord. He then went on to say that to call it by its technical name seemed very learned, but to a Roman the words foramen magnum meant merely a big hole. Pedantry never found a place with Dr. Leidy.

The last time that I saw him was in the autumn of 1886 when he attended the two hundred and fiftieth anniversary of the founding of Harvard College. He received at that time an honorary degree, and after the ceremonies were over Mr. Alexander Agassiz asked me to seek him out and escort him to the Museum of Comparative Zoölogy, where Mr. Agassiz was to meet him. I soon found Dr. Leidy among the University guests, and together in the beautiful autumn weather we walked up shaded Divinity Avenue to the Museum. He was full of interest in his surroundings and asked me about my work in the Harvard Natural History Laboratories and who my instructors were. When he learned that the Museum, the Laboratories, and the Zoological Library were all housed under one roof he greatly approved of the arrangement. He looked into our workrooms for a few moments, and after a brief inspection told me that he thought I had done well in coming to Harvard to continue my work in zoology. I then escorted him to Mr. Agassiz's office, where I left him. This was the last time I ever saw Dr. Leidy, for I was not often in Philadelphia after my removal to Cambridge and he died in 1891.

My appointment as a Jessup Fellow at the Philadelphia Academy extended over a period of two years and was completed in the autumn of 1882. At the expiration of this time, I was engaged by Mr. Tryon for work on his *Manual of Conchology*. Most of my time was spent on the volume of this publication that had to do with the cone shells—those beautifully colored, conical shells whose form so attracted Rembrandt that he made an exquisite etching of one of them, now a prize among collectors of his smaller works.

Shortly before my transfer to Mr. Tryon's employ my father, whose business prospects had improved little if any, strongly advised me to seek a college education and suggested in his characteristically uncompromising way Harvard University. Why? Father had two matters in mind. Harvard was an institution where a liberal education could be had and it was a center where Natural History had been highly developed, especially under Louis Agassiz. To most of my family the proposal seemed chimerical because of lack of funds, but my father's principle in such matters was to decide on what it was best to do and then to find the means of accomplishing it. Before I had had any idea of going to college, and shortly after I had left Friends' Central School, I had begun a kind of self-instruction. At home and at the Academy I had set aside short periods of time in which I worked on subjects that, had I remained at school, I would have been studying, and I surprised myself in discovering how much could be done in this way. I worked particularly in history and in German. After it was settled that I was to attempt to go to Harvard, I intensified these studies and used all my spare time in preparing myself for the Harvard entrance examinations. By an odd coincidence a set of these examinations was held in each June in the hall of the Academy, and in that month in 1882, a year before I expected to try for admission, I took pains to get all the information I could from the college examiner about the steps necessary in such a procedure. It so happened that the examiner in Philadelphia for that year was Professor W. M. Davis, who subsequently became a very close and valued friend. He told me much that I needed to know, but what heartened me most was his remark that any student who could spend one year at Harvard and demonstrate that he was of high quality would never be allowed to fall by the way because of lack of funds. I at once resolved to make every effort to have one year at Harvard, in the hope that I could thereby win for myself a continuation of college studies.

During my last year at the Academy I worked for Mr. Tryon by the hour, and did only enough to bring me in a very modest livelihood. All the rest of my time I put on preparation for the college entrance examinations. Through the generosity of an old business associate of my father's, I was enabled to take private lessons in Latin, from my former teacher in that subject at Friends' Central School; another one of my father's friends, a teacher of German at the University of Pennsylvania, helped me in that language. The rest of my preparation I attempted myself. It must not be supposed that I was a "greasy grind" and limited myself exclusively to pre-college studies. In those days the Philadelphia Orchestra performed each Thursday afternoon at the Academy of Fine Arts on Broad Street and gave an excellent program of classical music. A symphony was presented by playing one movement after another on each of four successive Thursdays, and then the whole symphony as a single piece was performed on the final and fifth Thursday. The rest of each program was made up of overtures, concert pieces, operatic selections, and the like, all of which made a very enjoyable afternoon of music. I attended these concerts regularly and had the pleasure of sitting with Mr. Tryon and his sister, Miss Adeline Tryon, who also came to the concerts regularly. The Tryons were both musical and they helped me much in maturing my early fondness for music. They were, moreover, cultivated and well traveled and their company was exhilarating and improving. I recall that at one program Miss Tryon pointed out to me, in the title of a piece of music, the German word *Hochzeit* and asked me, for she knew I was studying German, if I knew what it meant. I puzzled over it some time and then replied that it had something to do with a high time. She was greatly amused, confessed that the translation was not bad, and then told me the word meant wedding. My inability in this translation did not augur well for my Harvard entrance examination in German, but notwithstanding I passed in that language and the only consequence of my earlier blunder was that the meaning of *Hochzeit* has remained ineradicably with me.

It was customary in those days for candidates for admission to Harvard to divide their examinations and take one set of subjects in one year and the remainder the next year, but I attempted all the examinations at one period, a very trying ordeal. This was in the middle of June 1883. I waited in great suspense to hear the results of my endeavor, for I had been told that I should receive word of the outcome of the examination in about two weeks after it had taken place, but July went by and still no word. I was in great concern, almost in despair. Finally I wrote to the college, only to find out that a certain dean had gone on his vacation and left much work unattended to; but his secretary informed me that I had been admitted to the Lawrence Scientific School with conditions in Latin, Algebra, and Trigonometry. What a relief even with these deficiencies! Now came the task of finding the wherewithal for college expenses.

To such of my family who might have helped me with funds, the idea of going to Harvard was like going to perdition. Their attitude reminds me of the remark of a Swedish helper in the family of a friend of mine who declared of the son that "Master Walter could not decide whether he would go to Princeton or to Jail." I am sure that certain members of my family regarded going to Harvard as worse than going to jail, and that none of their resources would ever be squandered on such a step toward utter destruction. Again my father, though a ruined man in the eyes of the world, came to the rescue. He sought out an old business associate whom he had materially helped in earlier days and told him of our ambitions and our plight. The reply to this appeal was dictated, I am sure, by pure generosity, for no business man would have risked a twopence on me. He advanced me two hundred dollars without security and to be returned to him at my convenience. What a Providence! With this in my pocket I resolved to plunge into the great adventure. The absurdity of attempting to go to Harvard College on two hundred dollars of borrowed money! However, such is youth! Three years earlier I had started out in Philadelphia with nothing in my pocket at all. Was not two hundred dollars better than that even if it was borrowed money?

The New Life

AS ONCE OF OLD FROM IDA'S LOFTY HEIGHT
THE FLAMING SIGNAL FLASHED ACROSS THE NIGHT,
SO HARVARD'S BEACON SHEDS ITS UNSPENT RAYS
TILL EVERY WATCH-TOWER SHOWS ITS KINDLING BLAZE.

O. W. Holmes

IN the days of my college adventure, Philadelphia fences and wooden buildings had nailed upon them, here and there, brown slabs of wood which in black letters called upon all to take the Fall River Line for Boston. How that declaration echoed and reëchoed in my ears! Was I ever to follow its admonition? In 1883 Harvard College opened on the last Thursday in September, and as that date approached I found that my father had matured a plan for my migration to New England. He and I together were to go to Boston and Cambridge and, after he had seen me settled for the winter, he was to return to Philadelphia. My meager outfit for college was packed in a small trunk and sent in advance and father and I followed, first by train for New York and then by night boat for Boston. Whether we took the *Pilgrim* or the *Puritan* I do not remember, but whichever it was, the steamboat after much straining and creaking rounded Point Judith and brought us at a very early morning hour first to Newport and then to Fall River. Here we took the five o'clock boat train for Boston. As we left our port of landing the first morning light was breaking in the east, and I looked out on a dim countryside that seemed strange and novel. Rough, hummocky, stony, and often rocky, how different it was from the gently sloping hills and the rich, level fields of my native Pennsylvania! It gave the impression of a rugged and at times almost barren land. I began to understand how Nature had forced suffering on the Pilgrim wanderers. Later in college I was to learn that this whole region had been glaciated, a geological change that had stopped short of most of Pennsylvania. It was this scouring by the polar ice that had given New England, and in fact all the country northward, such striking topography. Over this stern and almost forbidding terrain, as dawn was breaking, we were transported without stop till we reached the Old Colony Depot in Boston. Father knew the town well, and in the early waking hours we walked through Washington Street to the neighborhood of City Hall. Here, in a restaurant almost in the shadow of the Old South Church, we had breakfast and then made our way very deliberately to Boston Common.

We carried a letter of introduction to Mr. Henry O. Houghton of the publishing house of Houghton, Mifflin & Company. Not to be too early in calling on Mr. Houghton, we walked about the common and father showed me where the ancient Great Elm had stood. By a mere coincidence, he had been in Boston in 1876 when this venerable tree had been blown down, and he had brought me a piece of its wood as a curio for my collection. When the time seemed ripe we went to Mr. Houghton's office on Park Street, opposite the common, and asked for him. He was a kindly, elderly gentleman who showed much interest in me when he learned that I was planning to enter Harvard. Father told him that I was a studious boy much inclined to stay too close to my books and my work, and that it was desirable that I find living accommodations some distance from the college so that I would be obliged to have a certain amount of fresh air and exercise each day in going and coming in my college affairs. Mr. Houghton quickly grasped the situation and called in one of his clerks, a Mr. Kimball, who boarded in Cambridge at what Mr. Houghton believed might be a suitable stopping place for me. On talking with Mr. Kimball, father favored the suggestion and after thanking Mr. Houghton we started for Bowdoin Square and the horsecar for Cambridge. The location of the boardinghouse to which we had been directed was on Main Street, now Massachusetts Avenue, in Cambridgeport. Here we met the kindly proprietress, Mrs. Dalton, and I soon found myself ensconced in a small, hall bedroom which with my meals would cost me the modest sum of five dollars a week. Thus settled, with unexpected quickness and satisfaction, father and I walked to the college grounds which were about a mile from my newly established quarters. This distance, if covered four times daily, seemed to meet father's views about exercise for me. Having now arranged the essentials of my way of living, and after a midday meal at Mrs. Dalton's, we set out sight-seeing.

Like all good pilgrims to this part of New England, we at once turned our steps toward Bunker Hill. We easily found the way to Charlestown and up the hill to the battleground. Together we climbed the Monument and had a superb view, in the fine afternoon light, of the city and its surroundings, the wide expanse of country-side, the adjoining towns, the Blue Hills to the south, and eastward the harbor and its islands. We left Bunker Hill in the late afternoon and I went with father to the Old Colony Depot where I saw him off on the boat train for the Fall River Line and the south. Alone in Boston I found my way back to the Cambridge horsecars and so to my new habitation. The enthusiasm of my Harvard adventure was growing on me. Had I not been at the top of Bunker Hill and looked down on Boston? and to look down on Boston, was not that a real conquest? If you ask a Bostonian where he is going, he is very likely to say to you down to New York or down East. Whichever way he goes from Boston it is always down, even though the city itself is not many feet above sea level. But to gain a situation where you yourself can declare that you look down on Boston is really something. From that time on the town is no longer formidable. To this situation I had attained. I understood then why visitors to this region almost at once rush off to ascend Bunker Hill.

The day following my arrival in Cambridge was devoted to college affairs. It was the opening day of the new term at Harvard. I was in a strange daze. Was this event that I had dreamed of for so long, this going to Harvard, actually coming to pass? At the office of the Lawrence Scientific School I was accepted as a student, and I was given an assortment of cards and pamphlets to guide me through the enchanting and bewildering maze of entrance formalities. No sub-freshman ever entered the new life that Harvard has to offer him with greater excitement than I did. I must have been, however, a great nuisance to my elders, for I made my way to most of those with whom I was to study only to be told by each that to join a given class I should present myself at the classroom or at the laboratory on the hour of the first appointed meeting of that class. Having thus done, in the course of my first day, all that I could imagine of my possible duties, I stopped and took breath. What had transpired? I had at last been admitted to the University of my father's choice!

Of all that I brought with me to Harvard nothing was so considerable as the volume of advice, suggestions, and warnings which had been generously heaped upon me as I was leaving Philadelphia. I was told that in a large University like Harvard I would find myself quite alone, neglected, and without companionship. I was also told that as a beginner in the natural sciences I must not expect to see anything of the luminaries whose names had made Harvard celebrated in these sciences. Asa Gray in botany, the younger Agassiz in zoology, and others of their caliber were not to be approached by a youngster like me. It was further pointed out to me that in the whole United States there were not more than half a dozen positions of the kind I was fitting myself to hold, and that vacancies in these positions were extremely rare. My good friend, Dr. Kinderdine, who had always taken a paternal interest in me, urged me not to attempt to earn a living in natural history, but to study medicine, practice the profession from Mondays till Fridays and recreate in natural history Saturdays and Sundays. This he believed was the only way in which the earning of a livelihood and the enjoyment of natural science could be brought together. Perhaps I was foolish in attempting to study at Harvard; it certainly seemed so to most of my advisers. But I closed my ears to much that they said and I resolved to see first of all what good training in my chosen field would do for me.

I began my natural history studies in the Lawrence Scientific School by taking one more course than those prescribed for the first year, thus making five courses in all. These included elementary work in such subjects as zoology, botany, physiography, and physics. The additional advanced course that I elected was one on the types of plants and animals, the only course with laboratory work which I had that year. The botanical part of the course was in the hands of Dr. W. G. Farlow, one of the most charming and interesting instructors I ever had, and the zoological part was conducted by Dr. Walter Faxon, already mentioned, a thorough New Englander full of the history and interesting traditions of the region. As an instructor he had a very direct and scholarly approach to his subject. In lecturing he had a trait that I never in my life saw approached by any other platform speaker: he could nap in his own lectures. Dr. Faxon's part of the course came in the second half-year when the spring sunshine was warm and the breezes gentle. Moreover, his particular lecture hour was at two o'clock, shortly after luncheon. He would enter the lecture room, take his seat behind the lecture table, and, after a few brief introductory remarks, he would fall into a succession of short statements punctuated by bowings of the head and closings of the eyelids. This sequence of events would constitute the body of the lecture. A passage from one of his talks to us might well be as follows, in which the dashes stand for the lowering and the raising of the head as interruptions in his speaking: "The fresh water hydra—is a very small animal —inhabiting our ponds and streams—and attached to floating vegetation," and so on. The remarkable part of Dr. Faxon's lecture technique was that the flow of his thought, notwithstanding the brief interruptions, was completely consistent and, what is more, proceeded at such a moderate rate that we as young students were just about able to keep up with it and transcribe it fully in our notebooks.

This proficiency, if somnolence of the kind here described can be so designated, recalls to my mind another academic lecture perhaps equally remarkable though in another direction. The report of this unique discourse came to me from an Italian student who stated that he was present at its delivery. In his opinion it was the briefest university lecture ever given. The lecturer was Dr. Angelo Mosso, Professor of Physiology at the University of Turin and Director of the laboratory on Monte Rosa for the study of mountain sickness and other physiological conditions in very high altitudes. Dr. Mosso was a very distinguished man and was entitled to the Italian designation of Senator. He lectured with much formality and éclat before his class. "Gentlemen," he said, "I shall lecture today on the muscles of mastication. There are three muscles of mastication, the masseter." Then after a considerable pause he repeated, "There are three muscles of mastication, the masseter." Again a lengthy pause. "The masseter." After this pause a student shouted "You don't know them." Whereupon Professor Mosso with great deliberation remarked: "I do, but I shall not mention them today," and the lecture was closed. This unusual discourse may well take its place next to Dr. Faxon's efforts, except that Dr. Mosso's lecture was a chef-d'œuvre whereas Dr. Faxon's performances were almost a habit.

Three events concluded my first year at Harvard, one very sad, and two encouraging. My father, despondent and much broken in health, died suddenly in the late spring of that year, 1884, and the family in Philadelphia was broken up. Thus in a way I was thrown, if possible, still more upon my own resources. Secondly, I had begun to earn money at Harvard by tutoring fellow students for their examinations. By keeping my own studies up I could coach others during the June examinations in the same courses that I was taking and thus review my own work and, what was equally important, earn considerable sums of money, for the charges for tutoring were relatively high. I was so fortunate in this work that I finished my first year in June 1884 without debt beyond the two hundred dollars that I had originally borrowed. The third and last event of my first year was my appointment to a scholarship for my second year in the Lawrence Scientific School. The amount of this scholarship was not large, but it was sufficient to cover my college tuition and on learning of my appointment to it I looked forward with fair confidence to another year at Harvard, for I felt sure that by tutoring I could earn enough to meet my living expenses for that year.

My first year at Harvard was not all study. There were, even within the University itself, many non-scholastic attractions. Of these the most inviting to me was exercise in the Hemenway Gymnasium. This was under the general supervision of a director, Dr. Dudley A. Sargent. Freshmen were advised to submit themselves for a physical examination by Dr. Sargent, and to follow his advice in taking regular gymnasium work. I applied for such an examination and a short time thereafter I was notified to appear at the office of the director. Here I was variously measured. I was six feet one inch in height and weighed some hundred and thirty-eight pounds. Dr. Sargent asked me to chin myself on the bars and I lifted myself, I believe, seven times, not because of my strength in particular, but rather, I suspect, in consequence of my very light weight. Dr. Sargent looked me over and told me that he doubted if my physique would see me through my first year in college. Nevertheless, he gave me a book in which a prescribed course of exercise was laid out for me, including dumbbells, parallel bars, chest weights, and the like to which I added, what I greatly enjoyed, running. On Holmes Field, next to the Gymnasium, Harvard had an excellent quarter-mile cinder track on which a number of us ran some two miles or so in the evening whenever the weather permitted. Although I kept up my physical exercises during the whole of my freshman year, and much to the advantage of my general health I am sure, I closed that year with the same height and about the same weight with which I had entered it. Thus, at the end of about the second decade of my life, I was obviously an undernourished, skin and bones stripling.

It was this bodily condition which had led Dr. Sargent to doubt my capacity to pull through my freshman year, but I did succeed in doing so; not only that, but I continued in that physical state till I was some thirty-three years old. Then, after a severe attack of influenza, my family physician declared I must do something about my general health. Thereupon my wife and I, for I had by then married, spent some three months at a fine, old farm, at the Ark, on very high land at the base of Mount Monadnock in New Hampshire. Here we had all that good country-life could afford us, a bountiful table with the best of farm produce, including milk and cream, excellent, high air, and as full an opportunity as anyone could wish for hard and enjoyable work in clearing out trash and cutting paths in the mountainside. To this kind of life the family of Dr. William Wesselhoeft, part of the settlement at the Ark, were much given, and they most generously introduced us to it. As a result of this summer's work and play on the side of Monadnock I changed my weight from about one hundred and forty to one hundred and seventy-five or more pounds, nor have I since dropped appreciably below this weight.

Some years after this physical transformation I renewed my acquaintance with Dr. Sargent, in a neighborly fashion through my sister, and when I related to him my early experiences in his office at the Hemenway Gymnasium he was much amused and confessed that I had clearly outgrown my insufficiencies.

Some Scientific Luminaries at Harvard

HE WAS A SCHOLAR, AND A RIPE AND GOOD ONE.

W. Shakespeare

THE first time I heard the name of Agassiz is strangely impressed upon my mind. I was about nine years old and my parents and I were at the corner of Seventh and Wallace streets, Philadelphia, where we were changing cars on our way to church. As we were standing there awaiting the car my father remarked that word had recently come of the death of Louis Agassiz. I asked him who Louis Agassiz was and he told me that he was a celebrated European naturalist who had been invited to this country and had settled finally in Cambridge, Massachusetts, where he had become Professor of Natural History at Harvard University. Father had a way of telling things so that they stayed by the hearer, and his simple statements about Louis Agassiz never left me. When I was a Jessup Fellow at the Philadelphia Academy of Natural Sciences it was rumored, on a certain morning, that Alexander Agassiz, the son of Louis Agassiz, would visit the Academy that day to arrange with John Ryder to become naturalist to the United States Fish Commission. I was working in the library when Mr. Agassiz arrived and I saw him as he was shown to Ryder's room. His step was quick and businesslike and after his visit he left as rapidly as he came. During my early undergraduate days at Harvard I went to a competition for the Boylston Prize in Elocution, and there I saw George Agassiz, Alexander Agassiz's son, win the prize. Thus, in these remote ways, I had early contacts with three generations of this distinguished family.

The year I came to Harvard, 1883, I found that all the instruction that I was to receive in zoology, in botany, and in physiography was given in the new section of the Museum of Comparative Zoölogy, constructed through the munificence of Alexander Agassiz and just opened. It contained the laboratories, lecture rooms, and studies of the professors in natural history, the zoological library, a part of the zoological museum, and the rooms of the director, Mr. Alexander Agassiz. In all respects it was beautifully appointed. It carried over with it from the earlier Agassiz days many notable items, among which the most interesting to me was Eli Goodrough, the janitor in Louis Agassiz's time. Eli soon taught me an important and, as I subsequently learned, worth-while distinction: Louis Agassiz was always to be referred to as Professor Agassiz and Alexander Agassiz as Mr. Agassiz. This rule I always followed, and yet Mr. as used with Mr. Agassiz came to mean very much more to me than Mr. spoken to anyone else. This simple title seemed always to appeal to Mr. Agassiz for he was a true democrat. I was told that when, as a young man, he first landed in this country he came ashore with a violin case under his arm; he had been obliged to practice on the instrument though he detested music. On landing he asked if this was a free country and on being told that it was, he smashed the violin over a pile-head at the wharf and threw it into the water. I am not assured of the authenticity of this act, but it is of the kind that Mr. Agassiz, as a man of strong democratic independence and of passionate nature, might well have done. Eli Goodrough, so far as I know, was the only person at the museum who would speak up to Mr. Agassiz, and Mr. Agassiz, though not a man to brook interference, would listen to Eli's comments as he would not have listened to those of any other person. In fact, I believe no one else in the whole establishment would have dared to speak to Mr. Agassiz as Eli did. Eli's remarks were always put respectfully, but they were at times in opposition to Mr. Agassiz's plans. That was the line over which Eli but no one else would pass. Eli acted always as though Mr. Agassiz were young and inexperienced, and Mr. Agassiz showed a certain consideration for Eli because, I believe, Eli had long been a faithful servant to his father, Louis Agassiz.

Eli never forgot Professor Agassiz and his ways. As a young instructor I once had a prepared lecture to give to a Radcliffe College class. The lecture illustrations were set up and I came to the museum just in time for the exercise. To my chagrin I found

that I had left my lecture notes locked up in a laboratory room for
which I had no key. I hurried to Eli in much concern and asked
him if he would open the room for me that I might get my notes.
He was always obliging and went at once with me and opened the
room, but as I was hurrying off with my manuscript he remarked:
"Professor Agassiz knew his subject so well that he could lecture
without notes." There is much to be said, however, about the two
ways of lecturing. This brings to my mind an account I once heard
of a young woman who wished to attend Professor Agassiz's Harvard lectures on natural history. The young woman, whom I knew
in her maturity as Mrs. Sabine, was the mother of the lamented
Professor Wallace C. Sabine, whose early death at the close of the
First World War deprived Harvard of a distinguished physicist. As
a young woman Mrs. Sabine came from Ohio to Boston for a
winter, as a part of her general education. On reaching her destination she immediately went to call on Professor Agassiz at the
museum to arrange for attendance at his winter lectures. She was
chagrined to learn that the lectures were given under the management of Harvard College, to which women were not admitted.
She expressed very great regret, for one of her chief objects in
coming to Boston and Cambridge was to hear Professor Agassiz's
discussions. For a moment or two Professor Agassiz was thoughtful,
and then he remarked that he lectured in such and such a hall in
the museum, that this hall had an exhibition gallery around its
upper story, and that according to his agreement with the Commonwealth of Massachusetts, this and other exhibition galleries in
the museum were open regularly to the public. If she cared to come
into this gallery at the time of his lecture, she could hear the lecture,
and no one would say her nay. She and Professor Agassiz parted in
friendly recognition of the solution of her difficulty, and at the
time of the first lecture, Mrs. Sabine found her way to the appointed
gallery. Here, much to her surprise, she discovered a chair awaiting
her. She used it, heard the lecture with comfort and satisfaction,
and found the chair again and again in the gallery on lecture days
during the winter. The account of this experience was given me by
Mrs. Sabine when, toward the close of her life, she was a resident of
Cambridge. I once made some remarks about it in the presence of
Eli Goodrough who immediately responded by saying: "Yes, and

I was the person who placed that chair in the gallery for the lady by Professor Agassiz's direction."

Mr. Agassiz never developed his father's faculty as a lecturer and a teacher. Trained as an engineer, matured as a financier, he was nevertheless a lifelong student and investigator in natural science. He worked almost exclusively with marine animals, and in his early investigations he devoted much attention to starfishes and to sea urchins. He undertook studies on the fossil representatives, as well as on the living members, of these groups of animals. His interests widened from marine creatures till they embraced the whole sea, the physiography of which as well as its organic contents came within his domain. The growth of coral islands, that problem which had perplexed naturalists since the days of Darwin, became uppermost in his mind and with Dr. W. M. Woodworth, Dr. A. G. Mayer, and especially Dr. H. B. Bigelow as assistants, he made many and extensive trips to the south seas till he had firsthand acquaintance with almost all the important groups of coral islands on the globe. His reports on these expeditions form a most significant contribution to the understanding of these strange organic islands and their method of formation. Thus, the ocean was his laboratory. An English colleague of his who was also a profound student of the sea, declared the younger Agassiz to be the Prince of Oceanographers.

To those of us about the natural history laboratories in the museum, Mr. Agassiz's figure was a familiar one as he came and went to his workrooms and office. These were his special preserves, and when he was away on expeditions or elsewhere, they were kept strictly closed till his return. They were in the particular care of an Irish janitor named James. During one of these periods when Mr. Agassiz was away there was a celebration in the United States in honor of the French Revolutionary Commander, Comte de Rochambeau. The French delegation appointed to carry out these formalities visited Harvard University, and President Eliot escorted its members to certain points that might be of special interest to them. Among the various places which they visited, was the Museum of Comparative Zoölogy which was shown as an example of what a French-Swiss father and son had done for Harvard. President Eliot planned to show them Mr. Agassiz's working quarters, and James was called to open the rooms; he responded by unlocking the door and letting the visitors look into the apartments, but he would not allow anyone to pass in, for he said he had been instructed by Mr. Agassiz that under no circumstances was he to admit anyone to these quarters. President Eliot asked if James knew who he was and he said: "Yes, you are President Eliot." After this limited peep into where Mr. Agassiz worked the party, under the guidance of the president, went their way. On Mr. Agassiz's return from wherever he happened to have been President Eliot wrote him a note, told him of the circumstance of the visit, and congratulated him on the kind of service he had from James. We were told that both President Eliot and Mr. Agassiz enjoyed the whole episode, each in his own way.

Mr. Agassiz certainly had a good sense of humor. On one occasion a meeting of the Visiting Committee in Geology was being held on the first floor of the museum, and as it was breaking up Professor Shaler, chairman of the department, spoke to a young instructor, Collier Cobb (who afterwards became Professor of Geology in the University of North Carolina) and asked him to see that Professor Pumpelly's coachman had the carriage ready for that member of the committee. Cobb in great haste rushed out on the museum steps, and seeing a man there asked him: "Are you Professor Pumpelly's coachman?" to which the person addressed replied: "No, I am Alexander Agassiz." This greatly amused Mr. Agassiz who related it to others, but it was a matter of much concern to poor Cobb, who finally took the joshing we gave him in good part.

Mr. Agassiz's generosity to the Harvard Corporation, and his intense interest in the museum led him to feel that the Harvard authorities were not so coöperative as he had hoped they would be. Having provided laboratories, studies, and other equipment, Mr. Agassiz expected the Harvard Corporation to appoint additional teachers in the natural sciences and to pay their salaries. This the corporation was very slow and reluctant to do. When I joined the teaching staff in zoology it consisted of Professor E. L. Mark and myself, and Mr. Agassiz described zoology at Harvard as being in the hands of a man and a boy, a very just statement.

Although Mr. Agassiz had his difficulties with the Harvard Corporation he was always most friendly and cordial to those of us who were doing advanced work in the museum. For my bachelor's degree in science I prepared a thesis on the structure and development of the eyes in the scorpion. This was put into form for the printer in the summer of 1887, and I then took it to Mr. Agassiz to submit it for publication in the *Bulletin* of the museum. I expected that he would set it aside for examination and let me have his decision later. Instead of this he looked it over at once, asked me some questions about the source of the material and about the text, and then, after looking over the plates, he wrote out an order to Mr. Meisel, the Boston lithographer who did the work for the museum, and told me to take my figures to the lithographer and explain to him what was needed. The quickness of Mr. Agassiz's decision almost took away my breath and, as this paper was my first zoological effort, the kind of reception it got at Mr. Agassiz's hands gave me a pleasure that I can scarcely express. As a member, and at one time President, of the Thursday Club Mr. Agassiz regularly invited a number of us to the fortnightly meetings of this body when they took place at his residence. Here we met a most interesting group of gentlemen from many walks of life, heard two or three brief and worth-while papers, after which we enjoyed a truly sumptuous repast. It would be difficult to imagine a more hospitable and kindly host than Mr. Agassiz on such occasions.

It was at such evening gatherings as those of the Thursday Club that I met many of the scientific men from the neighborhood of Boston. One of these, however, I became acquainted with very much earlier, in fact in my freshman year. This was the botanist, Dr. Asa Gray. My meeting with Dr. Gray was almost entirely accidental. The curator of the Botanical Section in the Philadelphia Academy of Natural Sciences was Mr. J. H. Redfield, with whom I, as a Jessup Fellow, was well acquainted. Mr. Redfield knew Dr. Gray intimately, and frequently sent packages of plants to Dr. Gray or received them from him. In those days I went back and forth several times a year between Cambridge and Philadelphia, and Mr. Redfield and then Dr. Gray found it convenient and in the interests of safety to use me as a messenger. Thus, in my undergraduate days, I was often carrying parcels of plants in one direction or the other. Dr. Gray welcomed this service and I in return, so to speak, found it very pleasant to become acquainted with Dr. Gray.

Dr. Gray died in 1888, but his widow continued to live in their old house in the Harvard Botanical Garden. As a newly married couple my wife and I came in 1894 to live in the neighborhood of the garden. We soon became acquainted with Mrs. Gray who invited us cordially to informal afternoon teas held each month at her garden residence. When she learned that I was well acquainted with Mr. Redfield she gave us an unusual account of a trip that she, Dr. Gray, and Mr. Redfield took in the South, I believe, in the Carolinas.

Dr. Gray was desirous of renewing his acquaintance with southern plants and of collecting material for his work on the flowering plants of the Eastern United States. He therefore proposed that he, Mrs. Gray, and Mr. Redfield make this trip with botanical objectives in view. As much of their exploring was to be in relatively unsettled country he engaged the services of an experienced local driver and outfit, and they did almost all their traveling by carriage. They were prepared in advance to rough it. Even Mr. Redfield, who was a very meticulous person, a Victorian of Victorians, understood this and assented to it. They met some unforeseen difficulties. Being northerners they were received in the South with some suspicion and were supposed to be Washington agents in search of "moonshiners," whose illicit distilleries were numerous in the less inhabited parts of the South. This not unnatural distrust was dissipated by Dr. Gray who gave out that they were herb-doctors in search of new remedies. After this word became noised abroad the expedition met with cordial treatment. Their driver endeavored day by day to bring them at the end of each journey to some town, or other small settlement, where at least simple hotel accommodations could be had. But on a certain stretch of travel he told them that this could not be done, and that he would be obliged to seek night-lodgings for them at an isolated farmhouse where he said they would find all arrangements very clean and orderly but very simple. They agreed to the proposal and arrived at the farmhouse toward suppertime. The farmer's wife received them cordially and they accepted her hospitality. The farmhouse, Mrs. Gray said, consisted so far as she could see of one enormous living room, with kitchen arrangements in one corner and the dining table in another. Along one side of the room was a row of beds. As the driver had promised, all was clean and orderly, but what they were to do for sleeping accommodations puzzled Mrs. Gray. After a good supper the family began to gape and it seemed to be time to retire. The farmer's wife then turned to Mrs. Gray and said: "Take your old man and go up that ladder and hunt a bed. You will find some on the platform." Mrs. Gray said she then saw for the first time a half-open attic over one end of the living room and provided with a ladder as a means of approach. Dr. Gray helped her up and she there discovered several beds all newly made and in best of order. Dr. Gray brought her some water, they washed, and crept into bed. What now was to happen to Mr. Redfield? Presently they heard him invited by the good woman of the house also to climb the ladder and hunt a bed. They watched from under the coverlets and presently Mr. Redfield's head appeared above the floor of the platform as he ascended the ladder. He stepped off the ladder and onto the floor, took a survey of the situation, and, after locating the Grays, he went to a bed as far from them as he could find and sat on the edge of this for some time. Mrs. Gray said they had great difficulty in restraining a giggle. Finally Mr. Redfield turned about and said: "Gray, I believe I shall take off my glasses." Mrs. Gray said they never discovered whether this was the limit of Mr. Redfield's undressing or not. They were soon asleep and when they awoke the next morning Mr. Redfield had already arisen and gone below. It was experiences of this kind that Mrs. Gray told my wife and me over her tea-cups and they gave us some insight into Dr. Gray's character and doings in his earlier days.

Asa Gray's importance as a scientific man rested not so much on his profound knowledge of the North American flora as on his very early espousal of Darwinism. He had corresponded on evolutionary matters with Darwin for a number of years before the publication of the *Origin of Species,* which was first issued in 1859, and when that volume made its appearance Gray was fully conversant with its contents. So completely had he mastered the subject that Darwin referred to him from time to time for the elucidation of complicated problems that had arisen in the discussion of natural selection, avowing that the subject had been more intimately thought out by Gray than it had been even by himself. Thus, from the start, Gray became a world-wide authority on Darwinism and was the first important scientific man in America to accept and publicly defend the doctrine. This was done by Gray at a time when to many churchmen the terms Darwinist and Atheist were said to be synonymous, a declaration which Gray stoutly and correctly declared to be untrue. This general stand on evolution gives some insight into the rigorous and sterling quality of Gray's mind, the more so as he was a member of the same university in which Louis Agassiz was teaching, a dominant and strong opponent of such views. The early advocacy of the Darwinian hypothesis will always remain as one of Asa Gray's most significant contributions to the general science of his day.

To the undergraduates of my time President Charles W. Eliot was an austere and forbidding personality. When we met him in the Harvard Yard we passed him without sign, for we knew that he did not wish to be troubled by us. As we became acquainted with him through his pronouncements and acts we came to regard him as cold and emotionless, something of a Stoic, in short a Puritan. This opinion of him was shared by many. Dean Shaler, under whom I sat for a term of years on the Administrative Board of the Lawrence Scientific School, once thrashed out a knotty question with us and then declared that our conclusion could not be followed up without the consent of the president. President Eliot was in his office overhead that evening and the dean proposed to get the president's consent then and there. He left us for a few moments and returned in great dudgeon. The president had declined to give permission. The dean was really wroth. He finally exploded in declaring the president a Puritan, a descriptive term that he preceded by an expletive that only a native of Kentucky would dare use about his superior.

President Eliot was certainly a Puritan, though not the last of that race; and notwithstanding his Puritanism he had a pronounced sense of humor. He was once called upon by the head of a midwestern college who, after some business talk, inquired whether he might ask the president a very personal question. Assent having been given, the visitor put his query: "Do any of the Harvard faculty ever call you to your face a liar?" To this President Eliot with a broad smile replied: "Oh, yes! and prove it on me too." Another instance in which the president made quick and amusing use of a situation was with Dean Shaler. The new bell to toll the hours for the Memorial Hall clock had just been set in operation, and Dean Shaler who lived almost under it had had little sleep during the night in consequence of this new and disturbing sound. He was ready at an early hour the next morning and rushed into the president's office with the explosive declaration: "Mr. President, either that bell goes or I go." Without entering into the excitement of the occasion President Eliot said quietly: "Where are you going, Mr. Shaler?" It was into this same presidential office where I had been called for business with the president that, with a burst of merriment, a granddaughter of his suddenly appeared. She threw her arm around his neck and reminded him of a promise to her that she hoped he would not forget. Business was set aside, the little lady pacified, after which the president with a smile returned to what we had been talking about. President Eliot was not all austerity.

Perhaps one of the most characteristic habits of President Eliot was that of continuous inquiry, of asking questions on all kinds of topics. I once received a telephone call from Mrs. Eliot who said that the president was slightly indisposed and held in the house by a cold, but that he would like very much to speak with me. I replied that I would come at once and I threw on my coat and left the laboratory. When I reached the Eliot house on Quincy Street and rang the bell, I was told by the maid that the president was confined to his bed and could not see visitors. Thereupon Mrs. Eliot appeared, asked me to come in and go up to the president's bedroom where I would find him expecting me. I went upstairs and found him in night attire, sitting bolt upright in bed. He motioned me to a chair and then said he had heard that I was building a new house, and that he would be glad to learn, if I would tell him, how I planned to pay for it. He had been thinking it over as he lay in bed and the information would be helpful to him. I was somewhat surprised and somewhat inwardly amused, but I fell to it. I told him what we had estimated the whole expense would be, that we had saved about half that amount, and expected to raise the other half by a mortgage. I outlined the house in general terms to him and told him that it was intended to accommodate my wife, myself, and my mother, and that it would of course have rooms for guests. For perhaps half an hour he talked over details of planning, construction, and raising money for the project and then he thanked me and I left him. I learned from this experience and others of a like kind that the president might call on any of us at any time for answers to questions of the most unexpected character and that it was well for us always to be ready with a full reply. Toward the end of his term of service, the president's portrait was painted and hung for a time in the Eliot parlor. Mrs. Eliot when she was showing it to us told us of their chore-man who on passing through the house had been called by her to see it. She asked him what he thought of it. The man was somewhat embarrassed but after standing first on one foot and then on the other he said: "Well Mrs. Eliot, he ain't asken no questions, is he?"

President Eliot's administration of Harvard University was unique, and I am grateful that my days of studentship fell within it. The president expected us to pay our university bills for which the corporation and the faculties would provide an abundance of inviting courses from which we could select our studies, and then whether we studied or not was our own affair. For the real scholar this was as near ideal as possible. For the loafer it also had its attractions, except that university life for him could not well be prolonged if he did not do at least some work. The amount of study demanded in those days was not large, probably not more than a half or even a third of what is expected today, but some of it must be done if the young man was to enjoy four years of college life. Almost full freedom was allowed. There were no roll calls in classes, but there was compulsory chapel. Even here, however, it was said, a substitute could be hired. I went to chapel when I first came to Harvard, but could find no section to which the scientific school students were assigned. I then asked our dean where such students sat in chapel. He looked at me with great contempt and remarked: "Scientific students have graduated in piety."

In my second year I took an advanced course in geology with Professor Davis. There were some ten students enrolled in this course which extended through the year. In December of the first term a new face appeared among us. Professor Davis said: "Who are you?" The newcomer replied: "William Randolph Hearst," which in those days meant nothing to us. Professor Davis asked further what Hearst intended by coming to the course at this season. Hearst said that he had signed for the course in September, had been in Florida ever since, and had now returned to make up his work. Professor Davis told him that such a plan was impossible. Hearst pleaded for admission and agreed to take any tutor Professor Davis would recommend. I was asked to undertake the work and agreed to do it. I told Hearst that we had eight field excursions to make up and that snow at any time might prevent this part of the program. We then talked over the requirements of the excursions and having understood the situation Hearst asked me to come to his rooms the following Sunday morning at seven and we would do as much as we could on that day. I came as appointed and he had a carriage with a pair of horses and a driver, and a substantial lunch for all three of us. We drove from well south of Cambridge, in Chestnut Hill, through the country to the westward and finally in the late afternoon into the northern section near Medford. By that time we had visited all eight quarries or other rock-exposures, and had made all the necessary observations and measurements. In about a day thereafter Hearst had his report completed, his geological sketch map drawn and handed all to the instructor. What made the field work such a quick operation under Hearst was the pair of horses and the fact that we drove from quarry to quarry in a circle around Cambridge instead of going out from Cambridge and back again for each locality as the class had done. Hearst and I traveled on the rim of a wheel, so to speak, and not out and back eight times on as many spokes. Professor Davis questioned me about Hearst's work and I assured him that it was done by Hearst himself and with an expedition and economy that was almost unbelievable. I also told him that I had never before tutored a man who had as quick and clear a mind, and as retentive a memory as Hearst had. It was a joy to work with such a fellow. I continued to tutor Hearst for the midyear and the final examinations, both of which he passed with credit. To a man of Hearst's mental capacity, the college work of those days was a mere bagatelle. He could do it and still spend half his college year in other pursuits. This whole performance by Hearst illustrates well what could be done by a student in President Eliot's Harvard. The system allowed the real student an almost ideal opportunity for his work, and consequently it bred such men as George Santayana. It also gave the roisterer full play. It likewise allowed the sluggard or the stupid one to slump on for a year or two and then to die in the traces, but to die for the most part unmolested. Free and irresponsible as the system was, I am sure that it had its advantages. Its large amount of freedom brought the student fresh from school and school restrictions suddenly into a rarer atmosphere and plunged him headlong into something that was very like real life. President Eliot stood behind much of this freedom.

In this chapter I have sketched three Harvard scientific luminaries of my time, Mr. Agassiz, Dr. Gray, and President Eliot. The Harvard of those days had of course many, many more, but there is not space here even to name them. The three whom I have mentioned helped give to Harvard University that preëminence which has long characterized it as an institution of learning. It was, and still is, a galaxy of intellectuals. In a playful way one is reminded of the reply made by an importuned Bostonian who at the beginning of this century was approached by an agent for the forthcoming first volume of *Who's Who in America*. After having listened to the description of the book, its uses, and its indispensableness, this native of the Hub burst out with: "Why do I need this *Who's Who*? I have the Harvard *Quinquennial Catalogue*." And so it appeared to me in my early days. Everything seemed to be in Harvard.

VIII

Too Many Masters

WE CANNOT ALL BE MASTERS

W. Shakespeare

MY first appointment to a teaching position in Harvard came in June 1886, when I was made assistant in zoology for the college year 1886–87, my senior year. Before I received this appointment President Eliot called me to his office and talked over my plans with me. He wished to know how I proposed to act as assistant and at the same time do my senior year's work for the bachelor's degree. I then told him what he was not aware of, that I had in three years almost completed my work for the degree and that though I planned to study further in my fourth year I was not obliged to do so to any great extent; thus I could easily devote one-half my time to assisting and use the remaining half for such study as I had to do. He seemed quite satisfied with this statement. Then he told me that he understood that I had a good reputation as a tutor among college students, and he asked me if I preferred the assistantship to tutoring and how much such a change would make in my earnings, for as an assistant in the college I was not allowed to tutor. I told him that I would make less money as an assistant than as a tutor, but that I nevertheless preferred the assistantship, for that was in the direction in which I wished finally to move. He asked me how much I made as a tutor and I told him that the best day I had ever had yielded me seventy dollars. He was much surprised at this and I explained to him that I could take as many as three students an hour at two dollars apiece and that I tutored, with omissions for meals, from eight in the morning till about ten at night. I assured him that the work was very tiring and for this reason, if for no other, I preferred assisting. I also pointed out that the times during which ordinary tutoring could be done were the two or three weeks of the midyear and of the final examination periods, when I too had to take examinations. He was amused when I told him that as a result of tutoring I knew one course, mineralogy, so fully that I received a grade of one hundred per cent in its final examination, my only perfect college grade. After this general conversation President Eliot informed me that he was satisfied with my replies and that I would be appointed to the assistantship, but he added as I was leaving him that the appointment was for one year only and that he did not wish me to think that I was wanted on the permanent staff. This last remark was in a measure a rebuff to me, and I puzzled over its meaning. As I learned by experience, such remarks were characteristic of the president and represented that side of him which gave to many the impression that he had a cold and bloodless nature. Perhaps he thought his remark might put me on my mettle. It certainly had something of that effect, for I resolved to teach to the best of my ability and to demonstrate, if possible, that my services were worth-while to the university. Thus I began my senior year as a half-time teacher in elementary zoology, and I ended that year with a reappointment to the same post for the following year.

During my four undergraduate years I had prospered reasonably from a money standpoint, for at the end of my last year I had paid off my original debt of two hundred dollars to my father's old business associate, and I was some four hundred dollars to the good in the Charles River Bank. Prospects looked better to me than when I had entered Harvard deficient physically, scholastically, and worse than deficient financially. I inwardly thanked Professor W. M. Davis many times for the encouraging words he had given me when, as a prospective candidate for admission to Harvard, I had been assured by him that if I could come to college for one year and show that I had quality as a scholar, Harvard would not let me drop out for want of material aid.

After the completion of my fourth year I received from Harvard, in June 1887, the degree of Bachelor of Science in Natural History. The next college year, 1887–88, was my first year as a graduate student. Again I served as half-time assistant and did half-time work on studies which I hoped would eventually lead to the degree of Doctor of Science. The year following I was advanced to instructor in zoology, and I had full charge of two courses, one on type-animals, and the other on the comparative anatomy of vertebrates, courses that as an undergraduate I had taken under Dr. Walter Faxon. I taught these courses well enough to be reappointed for two succeeding years, during which time I felt so well settled at Harvard that I arranged for my family, consisting of my mother and my two sisters, to come to Cambridge that we might be reunited as of old. This arrangement continued till June 1891, when I resigned from my position at Harvard and left Cambridge, where my family was now settled, for two years of study in Europe.

In my last year as an undergraduate at Harvard I was not only teaching and studying, but I was also serving in a minor capacity as biologist to the Massachusetts State Board of Health, a position to which I had been called by the chairman of the board, Dr. H. P. Walcott. At this time the state board had undertaken a general survey of the potable waters of the state, mainly from a chemical standpoint. The work was done at the Massachusetts Institute of Technology under the general supervision of Dr. T. M. Drown. It was deemed desirable that the extensive chemical examinations of these waters should be accompanied by some record of the microscopic animals and plants contained in them. I was assigned to the task of making these examinations, and for some two years or more I reported on the organisms, excepting the bacteria, in Massachusetts drinking water.

One notable advance in the management of the state's supply of this class of water came from my work. Many of the towns and smaller cities in Massachusetts drew their supplies of water from driven wells or other ground sources. These sources were usually located near small lakes or in the edges of streams and were supplied with what might be called naturally filtered ground-water. Almost without exception, these wells yielded excellent water free from microscopic plants and animals, but after this water had been stored for some time in the large, cylindrical, iron reservoirs on hilltops the water became more or less foul from the growth of microscopic green plants, algae, and if not unwholesome was at least very unpalatable. The contrast between the clear, spring-like water that came directly from the wells and the foulness of the same water after it had been stored in the iron reservoirs was most striking. I met a number of the superintendents of water systems in which there was trouble of this kind, and I pointed out to them that their difficulties arose from the growth and decay of microscopic green plants in their reservoirs. I told them further that the growth of these plants was dependent upon sunlight and that, in my opinion, if they excluded sunlight from their reservoirs they would stop the growth of the algae. My suggestion, I must admit, was met with nothing short of derision. I was a youngster and knew nothing about water supplies and they declared that sunlight was a purifier and as such should be admitted to the reservoirs. Finally, after much talking, I made a partial convert of the superintendent of the Brookline water supply, and he agreed after a lengthy conversation with me to empty his high-service reservoir, clean it thoroughly and, after putting a wooden roof on it, well enough built to exclude light, to refill the reservoir with pure well water and learn what would happen. Having accomplished the preliminary steps, he and I both examined the condition of the water in the closed reservoir week by week and found not the least return of green growth, nor any trace of foulness in the renovated supply. This favorable state continued and after some months the superintendent agreed with me that we had solved the difficulty. He was delighted with the result as was I. He was free from complaints from the consumers of the Brookline water and I took pleasure in seeing my plan work out satisfactorily. A report on the matter was given to the state board of health and from that time forward all towns and cities in the commonwealth were advised to cover their ground-water reservoirs and to keep them proof against sunlight. The method proved fully satisfactory, and I must say that as I have traveled about I have taken great pleasure to note the universal presence of roofs on the ground-water supplies of the state. This was my one contribution to the potable water problem, but it was one in which I took some pride.

Besides teaching in Harvard and acting as biologist to the Massachusetts State Board of Health, I was registered as a graduate student in college and was doing research work there, and otherwise preparing myself to come up for a doctor's degree. I did my work under Dr. E. L. Mark, in whose laboratory I soon found myself associated with two other graduate students in zoology, Herbert H. Field and Charles B. Davenport. We had been preceded in this laboratory by a few other students, among them Dr. Howard Ayers, Dr. William Patten, and Dr. W. A. Locy; but we were the three who began that long line of zoological aspirants who frequented the Harvard zoological laboratory and who came under Dr. Mark's especial care. His method of treating advanced students was not peculiar, but very thorough. From the time you took your research problem under him till the last punctuation point marking the completion of your printed thesis you were under Dr. Mark's eye. The result of this personal attention was that he brought up the most devoted body of students that I have ever met. Even the least promising of them, for he helped these rather more than the others, were loyally attached to him. I have often suspected that his unstinted aid to them was given in consequence of the bitter loneliness that he himself suffered as a beginner in academic life, and of the way in which that suffering was dissipated by a genial and friendly German *Geheimrat* in zoology, Professor Rudolph Leuckart, under whom Dr. Mark studied and took his doctor's degree at Leipzig. It was in this friendly atmosphere at the Harvard zoological laboratory that Field, Davenport, and I started our advanced zoological careers.

Even today there is much to be said on the question of how should beginners in scientific research be treated? Dr. Mark certainly represented one extreme method. I think I never met another teacher of maturing scientific students who used so extreme a method as his, except perhaps Professor Carl Ludwig of Leipzig. He, like Professor Mark, took the utmost care in training personally those who studied under him. When, in 1891, I attended Ludwig's lectures in physiology at Leipzig I was told of an amusing experience that illustrated this relation to students. An American worker in Ludwig's laboratory, subsequently professor of physiology at the University of Michigan, had with much care, and with more or less help from Ludwig, completed a research which the student then put into the best German at his command. He thereupon handed his paper to Ludwig in the hope that it could be published. Ludwig kept the manuscript some weeks and then returned it to the student fully revised and written in excellent German. The young man was much embarrassed by all the care that Ludwig had taken in the matter and said that he did not feel free to publish the article under his name alone. Professor Ludwig brushed the matter aside and said very generously that of course the article should appear under the student's name. On further protestation from the young man, Professor Ludwig, who had a delicate sense of humor, remarked: "And if you do not soon publish another article as good as this perhaps some of your associates will begin to think you did not do this one all yourself." Such is the danger run by that system of over attention to students, but Ludwig was able to point to its remedy. The other extreme method of dealing with research students kills off the poor ones and develops great independence and originality in the others. It is the method that was used by the celebrated physicist, Professor H. A. Rowland of Johns Hopkins University. When he was asked how he had developed from those who worked with him such remarkable physicists he replied: "By neglecting them." What is best for a beginner in scientific research is still a problem. Too much nursing is certainly bad and perhaps too much neglect also. In my opinion a student, like other human beings, is for the most part born for what he is to be and the best that a teacher can do for him is to give him a stimulating and congenial environment wherein he can grow.

During the four years that I worked as a graduate student at Harvard I spent most of my time in studying the compound eye, an organ especially characteristic of crustaceans and insects. In June 1891 I presented to the Committee on Higher Degrees in Natural History a thesis in the structure of these eyes in crustaceans. In this thesis, which was published in the *Bulletin* of the museum, I differed radically from the most recent work on the way in which the nerves of vision ended in these eyes. Notwithstanding this departure, my thesis was accepted and after an examination I was awarded the degree of Doctor of Science.

My results seem to have been well founded, for they represent the current opinion of today. In 1896 when my wife and I went abroad for the summer we visited the physiological laboratory of the University of Vienna, the director of which was Professor Sigmund Exner, at that time the most distinguished physiologist of the compound eye in animals. He welcomed us kindly, showed us a number of interesting things in his workrooms, among them the view from a laboratory window that he had photographed through the eye of a firefly. As he gradually learned who I was he complimented me on my recent papers which he seemed to know, and remarked that in his opinion they were better than the less beautiful studies by another author, naming my chief opponent.

Professor Exner then apologized for not inviting us to his house for some further acquaintance, but he said his family and he were leaving in two days to go to Ischl in the Salzkammergut for vacation. We compared notes and found that we were to be on the same train out from Vienna. He then proposed that at the first long stop he and I should come out of the railroad carriages and meet on the station platform. This we did and he took me to the compartment where Frau Exner was, introduced me to her, and proposed that I ride with her to the next long stop a half-hour or so away. Before I went into the Exner compartment I conducted Professor Exner to our place on the train where Mrs. Parker was and left him with her till the appointed stop. As we exchanged places I had a last word with Professor Exner on the platform and he asked me whether his wife had introduced me to the elderly gentleman who sat in the corner of their section. I replied in the affirmative, but said that I did not catch the name and that after a few moments' conversation with him I found he wished to be left alone. "Yes," said Professor Exner, "he is not well. That was the composer Brahms. We always go together to Ischl for an outing." I was dumbfounded that without knowing it I should have been talking to the composer of those four beautiful symphonies which, as someone has rightly said, might well be ranked with the symphonies of Beethoven. This, as I have said, was in 1896. The next year Brahms died. Our Viennese visit ended in a dream, though only a dream, of music.

Although I am not in any sense a musician, it has been my fortune to make accidental and strange acquaintances with musical geniuses. In a way I may claim to have had a handshaking meeting with Johann Sebastian Bach. This might seem too extravagant a statement to be possible and yet in a measure it is true. I was in Leipzig at the time when the Johannis-Kirche was undergoing extensive repairs. It was known that Bach had been buried in the cemetery connected with this church and next to a certain wall. When the foundations for this wall were in process of being rebuilt the workmen were notified to look with care for an oak coffin with a metal plate on it, and to report to the authorities anything of the kind that was discovered. Such a coffin was found, though the metal plate on it was so far corroded as to be illegible. The contents of the coffin were carefully transferred to Professor His's anatomical laboratory in the university. Here the skeleton contained in the coffin was carefully reassembled and examined. From the state of the bones that made it up, the age, sex, and stature of the individual were determined with probability. The ear bones showed that this elderly man had had good hearing to the end of his life. With the skull as a base a papier-mâché model of the face was then constructed. All these elements conspired to show that this was the long-lost skeleton of Johann Sebastian Bach. When I was first in Leipzig in 1891 I had been a student in Professor His's lectures on embryology, and on this later visit I called on him in his laboratory. Thinking that I would be interested in such matters he was good enough to show me Bach's skeleton, now carefully laid out upon a table. I looked at the bones with true reverence, for I had always had a profound feeling for Bach's music. I asked Professor His if I might touch the scattered bones of the hand and he assented. Thus in a way I have a handshaking acquaintance with this master of great music. As is well known, the remains of Bach after this identification were returned to the Johannis-Kirche and now rest in an identified vault.

But I have wandered far from my instructorship in zoology at Harvard. This, as I have already said, I resigned in June 1891 when I received a doctor's degree in science from Harvard and was appointed by the university to a Parker Traveling Fellowship. Thus I left Cambridge for European study after four graduate years of most strenuous work, in which I had tried to fill at the same time three positions and satisfy as many masters. As a teacher I had worked for the zoological department of Harvard, as a biologist I had served the Massachusetts State Board of Health, and as a student I had endeavored to do scientific research that would entitle me to write a doctor's degree after my name. All had been accomplished, but I had served under too many masters and I was most relieved when the strain was over. Now I looked forward to one or perhaps more years of European travel and study when with changing surroundings, academic and otherwise, I could continue with composure to grow as a zoologist.

IX

Europe Beckons

THE TIME INVITES YOU
W. Shakespeare

IN making my plans to go abroad I had no idea of imitating the grand tours of a century or more ago through France, Switzerland, and Italy; nor even a Sentimental Journey through a part of these regions, and surely not one in which I was to be holding a pretty little French lady's hand through some five chapters in a book. My object was much more prosaic than such adventures, and yet there was romance in it all. I could not claim the distinction that Will Rogers did of having ancestors who stood on the shores of the Atlantic and welcomed the Pilgrim fathers. All my forebears came in vessels from the old country, almost all from England with a slight strain of Welsh and North German. My own name, Howard Parker, is suggestive of Anglo-Saxon stock, but as a matter of fact I can trace back the Parkers of my immediate family for only a few generations, and all of these were Pennsylvania Quaker farmers. There is a tradition that our branch of Parkers came from the region about old Boston in England. When I was last in the British Isles, in 1930, I made it a point to visit this Boston perhaps, however, as much to climb "The Stump" as for any other reason. On leaving the train at the English Boston I walked to its parish church, not through the principal street of the town, but over the less frequented byways and passages, and here on the door of a small house I saw much to my surprise a large brass plate bearing the inscription G. W. Parker and Son. Thus my father and I seemed to be still identified with this part of the country. After I had come down from "The Stump," I asked the old custodian who had sold me the ticket for admission whether he knew the people of the town, and he declared that he surely did, all of them. I then inquired who were G. W. Parker and Son and with a broad smile he said: "Mr.

Parker is a merry, little undertaker and has buried many a body from this Church." I thanked him for the information and went my way. Was I getting near my ancestral, if not my funereal soil? I have never felt for Europe, and particularly for England, what the dictionary authors call a nostalgia, but England was the place of my racial beginnings and in planning to go there, though mainly on a scientific quest, I went with a certain feeling of romance.

During my eight years at Harvard I had not only acquired a good preparation in zoology, but I had added much to my general education. About a quarter of my time at college had been spent on subjects that were not directly connected with my professional training. This, I am sure, is as my father would have had it, though it sometimes had the appeal of stolen fruit to me. I certainly was eager to make use of all the general opportunities that Harvard offered to its members for outside enjoyment. With me these extraneous interests often started in work that was obviously professional. As a student in the natural sciences I was required to take a course in freehand drawing. The lectures in this course were given by Professor Charles Herbert Moore and consisted of a brief outline of European painting. This subject was presented in such a way as to awaken in me an active interest in the Italian, Dutch, French, and English schools of art. I further attended, with great pleasure and benefit, Professor Charles Eliot Norton's courses on church building in the middle ages and on Greek art, both of which were presented with broad cultural implications. In all these courses it was suggested that we find our illustrations from the collections of the Boston Museum of Fine Arts, then in its formative stages at the old building in Copley Square, and this suggestion led to what proved for me to be both stimulating and enjoyable. Another local institution that added to my general pleasure was the Boston Symphony Orchestra. This musical organization, founded and for many years supported by Major Henry L. Higginson, was sought out by me on my arrival in Boston from Philadelphia, and for the modest sum of five dollars I succeeded in getting a good seat for its twenty-four Friday afternoon rehearsals. This was during the second year of these justly celebrated performers, then under the baton of its first conductor, Georg Henschel. At Harvard there was a growing musical center under Professor John Knowles Paine, who during one of my early winters gave a series of lectures on the history of music which any student not in the music department could attend for a small fee. These lectures were illustrated by Professor Paine at the piano, by a small group of musicians, mostly from the Boston orchestra, and by a quartet of voices. The quartet came from a church in a neighboring town and the soprano, who was a very sprightly young woman, was popular with the Harvard students. She was Emma Eames, afterwards to become famous in the Paris opera. We had no idea at the time to what a celebrated voice we were listening. I also attended during one of these winters Professor Francis James Child's readings from *The Canterbury Tales,* and thus got my first taste of Chaucer. In these, and a score of other ways, the growth of my college stature was added to. I did all this with delight and enthusiasm, and as maturity came I acquired an intense longing to see and experience many things that I had read or heard about. My desire was not that of a simple sightseer, but of one who had done everything except the real thing. To walk on London Bridge, to visit the collections in the British Museum, to see Notre Dame in Paris, and the Jardin des Plantes where Cuvier had worked, to look at Johannes Müller's laboratory in Berlin, at the spot where Vesalius had taught and worked in Basel, to visit the great art and scientific centers of North Italy, Venice, Florence, and Pisa with its leaning tower and traditions of Galileo, Rome with the history of ages behind it, and last of all to see the beauty of Naples and the Mediterranean—these were the experiences that Harvard had taught me to long for and these I was hoping to know at first hand. Still further I wished to see, and perhaps make the acquaintance of, those scholars who were at the head of the zoological profession and whose work stood to me as a model and foundation on which to build for the future. It was the dream of maturing youth, and it came at a time of life when no other intellectual call could quite equal it. This is what Europe held out to me in the days of the early nineties.

I sailed from New York for Rotterdam in a small Dutch steamer, the *Werkendam,* on the night of July 3, 1891. The boat was expected to take two weeks for the transatlantic crossing. We woke up well out at sea in relatively quiet water on the morning of the Glorious Fourth. Our Dutch captain ordered the *Werkendam* decorated with flags, gave us a good dinner, and in the early evening took to himself the prettiest girl on the boat and with these two at the head of a procession, and escorted by a band, we marched round the deck in pairs with colored fire and rockets till we felt we had celebrated with full rites the signing of our Declaration of Independence. A few miles off to the northward another steamer bound inward passed us with rockets galore. Thus was our great American holiday celebrated. Some two years later I was returning from Europe to America, and by the merest chance on the *Werkendam* with the same Dutch captain. It was mid-summer, there were few first-class passengers, and we were all at the captain's table. I remarked that I had crossed on this boat before and described the trip. The captain boiled up like a thunder cloud, let fly a Dutch oath, and then told me that the other steamer that we had passed and that we supposed to be celebrating the Fourth was really broken down and was signaling for a tow to New York. Had he been on the bridge where he should have been and not playing with the passengers he would have gone to the help of the other vessel, towed her back to New York, and lined his pockets with his share of the salvage money.

We had a quiet, uneventful crossing. When we were in fog I could not see that we slowed down, and I asked the captain if it was not the rule to run half-speed in fog. He smiled and said it was, but that when the *Werkendam* was doing her best she was not up to half-speed of an ordinary liner. Hence he did not change speed in foggy weather. He then added that if in such weather we struck a fisherman she would be more likely to stick on our bow longer, running as we did, than if we were going at a slower rate, and that this would give her men a better chance than otherwise to clamber onto the *Werkendam* before their vessel slipped off, a humane motive. But we hit nothing, maintained our speed, and saw the Lizard Light on the southwest corner of England within an hour of the predicted time. Most of that day we skirted along the southern shore of England, but so far away that little could be seen clearly. Hastings, where William the Conqueror entered England, was pointed out to me, after which we were in darkness. The next morning we were all up early to find that we were entering the Dutch Maas between the windmill-beset banks of which we slowly steamed. I asked the purser of the *Werkendam* with whom I had become intimate if the boat landed us at Rotterdam, to which he replied in the negative and on being further importuned about our landing-place gave forth a tremendously rough, guttural, rattling of R's with explosive violence ending in something like dam. I decided finally that he was not swearing but that this was his way of pronouncing Rotterdam, which was as far from mine as day is from night. I knew then that I was entering a land with a foreign language of which I knew not a single word. However I was not embarrassed for I was still among English-speaking people and I was to have quickly my first lesson in Dutch.

My heavy luggage had been sent from America to my German destination, so that on the *Werkendam* I had only very light handbags. These were quickly examined by the Dutch officials, and as there were almost no other formalities in entering Holland I was very soon off the dock and on the street. I had scarcely been there two minutes when a small boy, running at full speed with a bag of books over his shoulder, nearly collided with me. He stopped suddenly, looked up and said as near as I can represent it: "Who laht is et?" I said to myself, Dutch schoolboys are as likely to be late as American. I took out my watch which fortunately had local time and he looked at it, smiled at me, and ran on. *"Who laht is et?"* "how late is it?" my first Dutch lesson and I have never forgotten it. When a few years ago an Amsterdam friend of mine, Dr. Arien-Kappers, was visiting me I remarked that I knew almost no Dutch, but that I had one expression which I should like to try on him to see if it was recognizable. I then said: "Who laht is et?" at which he laughed and remarked that that was the way of asking in Dutch the time of day.

X

On Teutonic Soil

ICH WEISS NICHT, WAS SOLL ES BEDEUTEN,
DASS ICH SO TRAURIG BIN.

H. Heine

MY immediate concern on the Continent was not with the Dutch language but with the German. From school days, when I had first begun Latin and German, foreign languages had been my bête noire. I worked at them till I cried, for I had no success; I could never bring myself to love *amo, amas, amat.* The lowest grade I ever received in Harvard was in German. It was the lowest passing mark, and now German was to be the key for my further studies at Leipzig and probably other German universities. Hence I had come abroad early in the summer of 1891 with the intention of spending some six or eight weeks in a purely German atmosphere hoping that ear and tongue in that time might get trained in a language essential to me. Of course I read German without great difficulty, but as a spoken language I understood it only indifferently. Moreover, what I did speak was of a very unconversational kind. I remember a young German school teacher from Hanover who once asked me when I was studying conversational German what as a student I had done in the American university I attended. It took me some time to understand her question, though she doubtless put it in simple German, and when at last I did grasp it, I said: "Ich machte entwicklungsgeschichtliche Untersuchungen über Sinnesorgane." She was amazed and said to a mutual friend standing near us that Herr Parker could use German words that she could scarcely understand and yet he seemed hardly able to say *Ya* und *Nein!* I was in reality provided with a very limited vocabulary of almost useless academic German which had to be expanded in some way into the language of the market place. Could

I do in six or eight weeks in Germany what I had failed to do in as many years at school and college?

From Rotterdam I took passage on a small steamboat to go up the Maas and the Rhein to Düsseldorf. We made a number of stops, the most interesting of which was at Emmerich, for we arrived at this German customs port the same day as the Archbishop of Cologne, who was making his annual visitation. Our boat was to be tied up for most of the day so we were free to see such ceremonies as the town had to show us. The whole countryside had come within its gates and Emmerich was crowded to bursting. What a strange medley of costumes we saw, for everyone was appareled for the celebration! The great throng filled the narrow crooked streets and passageways, bounded by the irregular rows of centuries-old plaster houses, which led finally into the market place near which stood the Aldegundis church, the bells of which filled the air with sonorous peals. Such a spectacle I had never seen before in all my life. It was like some grand stage setting, but a thousand times magnified. Soon a hush came. The crowd of spectators in the main street was pressed back solidly against the house fronts and down the passageway thus formed in the center of the road, the ecclesiastical procession came. With slow, solemn steps and in full canonicals the church dignitaries approached; in their midst the Archbishop of Cologne, under a broad canopy supported by six poles in the hands of trusty bearers, walked reverently and slowly, blessing the people to right and left. As the procession drew near the throng went on its knees, and remained there, the men with caps in hand till all had passed. Then everyone flocked to the church into which the procession had passed and which had for hours been crowded to the doors. Yet for religious purposes it seemed sufficient to stand bareheaded in the warm sunshine outside the edifice, letting the benediction reach each one from afar. I had learned in early geography studies that the Rhine Valley was predominantly Catholic, but I had never known what such a statement meant till I had witnessed the coming of the Archbishop of Cologne to Emmerich. Thus ended my first day on Teutonic soil, a medieval, religious ceremony rather than a modern, scientific exposition.

Our little steamboat left Emmerich in the late afternoon and headed up the Rhine. The next morning we were at Düsseldorf where I parted company with the craft, betook myself to the main railway station, and, after an early midday meal, boarded a train for the Harz Mountains, my stopping place for the summer. On consulting the timetable I found it would be convenient to stop overnight at Soest. Here I left the train in the late afternoon, made my way to the center of the town, bag in hand, and found an agreeable room at the Deutsches Haus. This was a modest but very comfortable inn with a pretty garden and an agreeable proprietor. I was again impressed, as at Emmerich, with the quaintness of the town. After supper I walked out and around the ramparts which were mostly still standing and which the town had not grown much beyond.

The next morning the host of the hotel, knowing that I had a few hours before train time, suggested a visit to some churches. In one of these workmen were removing Reformation whitewash from what had been an earlier surface of wall beautifully ornamented in colors. Interested in the operation I uncovered perhaps a square foot of this ancient surface by picking off the whitewash with my fingernail, thus bringing to light beauty that had been hidden for centuries. In one of the smaller churches a strange local sign was pointed out to me in a large picture of the last supper of Our Lord: the outline of a Westphalian ham on the table, an element that must have seemed perfectly congruous to any inhabitant of ancient Soest. As I walked to my train I carried with me the impression that modern Europe was not unlike the whitewash coating that I had been picking off the church wall, a thin covering which was hiding the beauty of antiquity. I took the morning train from Soest, changed cars at Scharzfeld, and, in the afternoon, was in St. Andreasberg where an uneven contest between the German language and me was to be waged for the next two months.

St. Andreasberg is a pleasant Prussian town of some two thousand feet elevation in the Harz Mountains and noted for its salubrious air, its neighboring silver mines, and its canary birds. I had been advised to go there by my friend, Professor Theodore W. Richards, who some years before had spent a summer at a German pension in St. Andreasberg when he was acquiring spoken German. The pension was kept by a cultivated German lady, Frau Eugenie Garbe, whose son was a university professor, but who herself preferred the independence of her mountain retreat where she lived a very simple life with a congenial group of *pensionnaires*. Almost all those with her were Germans and I can testify that for long periods of time, day in and day out, nothing was to be heard at Frau Garbe's but German. Of course there was no agreement about this, but there could have been few places where a person would have been more fully steeped with German than in this pension. Moreover, it was pervaded by a very friendly atmosphere and of the Germans there, several of them teachers, all were more than kind to me in helping me with their language. One would hear me read, another would correct my written exercises, and a third would take me to walk and help me in conversation. Richards could not have directed me to a better place for the purpose in view. My progress was slow, but it was steady and I began to have confidence that in the end I would understand spoken German and be able to make myself understood in that language. I made one strange discovery. When I first came to Frau Garbe's there were at her pension only women, unmarried and married, and all my conversation was with them. After a few weeks, the husband of a lady, Frau Debray, arrived for a weekend visit. I was introduced to him, and though I had begun to speak to Frau Debray with some understanding I was quite at a loss to speak with Herr Debray. His German seemed to be of an entirely different order. His words, his constructions, his whole linguistic make-up was of a different kind from what I had been accustomed to. When his little son, Arthur, arrived on the scene I found I could talk with him as I could with his mother, but the father was for a while a complete stumbling block to me. As the season went on more husbands, and other men, came and I was gradually broken into the masculine ways of speech, but in the beginning my experience with the language of the German male gave me a real shock.

The Harz Mountains afforded delightful opportunities for tramping, as Heine had discovered in earlier days, and the *pensionnaires* at Frau Garbe's took many enjoyable hikes when I was there. To go from St. Andreasberg to the top of the Brocken, the highest mountain in the Harz, and back in a day was an easy excursion. On one occasion I walked in one day over the Brocken and down on the north side into Goslar where one of our Harvard staff in botany, Professor John G. Jack, was staying for the summer. I spent the night with him and the next day walked again over the Brocken back to St. Andreasberg. In this way I began to develop independence in my flights from my adopted mountain home. But my grand migration was to Halle on the Saale. Here in the early autumn of that year, 1891, a general scientific meeting was to be held, and as the professor of zoology at the university in Halle, Hermann Grenacher, was one whom I wished especially to meet, I resolved to go to the assembly. Halle was only a few hours' ride from St. Andreasberg and I was soon at my destination and comfortably settled. I took the necessary steps to join the association, but I cannot say that I understood much of its learned discussions. I did, however, enjoy its social entertainments. I took part in a float of a great chain of flatboats which by some power or other was drawn first up and then down the Saale. I was given a place in Professor Grenacher's boat, but he spoke not a word of English and, as I discovered in the end, my small amount of conversational German soon broke down before a very self-contained Professor. We crashed upon his question to me: "Wie gefällt es Ihnen hier?" This he put to me several times, at each repetition more slowly, but I was as impervious to it as a duck to water. Finally, embarrassed and in desperation, I asked if anyone in our boat spoke English, whereupon Professor Grenacher's assistant, Dr. Hesse, who was in one corner of our craft answered up and said the professor wished to know how it pleased me here. I wanted to say "fearfully," but instead, and with the hope that the question he had put to me some ten minutes before was still in his mind, I said "Sehr viel" and then lapsed into complete silence. Conversation was not for us, but I had made the acquaintance of Professor Grenacher. The German interrogation "Wie gefällt es Ihnen hier?" was seared into my soul never to be obliterated. I learned later that Professor Grenacher was a sick man and that he talked very little even with his near associates. I was saddened to read of his death a few years later.

My great Halle adventure, however, was not in Halle itself, but had to do with my return to St. Andreasberg. After I had settled my hotel bill at Halle, dispersed such *Trinkgeld* as seemed proper, and gone to the railroad station, I found that I lacked sufficient money to purchase an ordinary second-class ticket to St. Andreasberg. The best I could do with the pittance I had left was to buy a fourth-class ticket from Halle to Walkenried, which was some twelve miles short of St. Andreasberg. I went to the train and entered the fourth-class car. It was a simple wooden boxcar with win-

dows but without seats. There were a few upright posts from floor
to ceiling by which passengers could steady themselves if they were
standing. Several Germans of the working class were already in the
car. Some were sitting on their bags, or baskets, with their backs
against the sides, others were standing. After getting under way
we made numerous stops and I noticed that when a woman came
into the fourth-class a man would usually help her release the basket
or *Kiepe* from her back and set it on the floor for her. This seemed
to be the common courtesy of the place. When a proper moment
offered, I helped a woman slip off her *Kiepe*. She sat down next me
and I tried some conversation. We understood each other fairly
well. She told me that her family made homespun cloth, of which
she had several rolls in her basket, and twice a week or so she went
on the road to sell it. It looked like good substantial cloth for outer
garments. Pointing to my bag she asked me what I was selling. I
told her I was not selling anything, but that I had come from
America to study in Germany. I soon found that she had almost no
idea of America, of the ocean between it and us, and of the aims
and desires of a student. She did not travel far. When she arose I
helped her on with her *Kiepe*, said good-by to her, and saw her start
down a country road in search, I suppose, of customers. Soon, a
little before midday, we were at Walkenried. I left the train and sat
down in the small railway station to look over my guidebook for
the correct start for St. Andreasberg. The stationmaster was a
kindly soul and began to talk to me. I told him I was without
money and planned to finish my journey to St. Andreasberg on
foot. He conducted a small eating-stand in the station, and it occurred to me that I had some German postage stamps in my wallet.
Could these be exchanged for food? Surely, he said, they were as
good as money. I counted out my store of stamps, about thirty-five
pfennigs' worth, for which he gave me a large ham sandwich and a
glass of milk. We became very friendly and he advised me to visit
the ruins of a large Cistercian monastery in Walkenried before I
left. The ruins were very near the railroad station and he was acting
as custodian. I told him, as in fact he knew, that I had no money,
nor even stamps, for an entrance fee, but he waved this aside and
said I might go in free. I enjoyed nearly an hour walking over the
extensive ruins of the Cistercian church, and especially over a
beautiful cloister. This was apparently one of the most outlying

of the Cistercian establishments in its day and was of very considerable proportions. After my sight-seeing I thanked the station master for his kind advice and aid, picked up my bag, and betook myself to the road. The Cistercians were an order noted for hard work, frugality, even asceticism. Had I been unconsciously permeated by their spirit? On a meager diet with a wallet devoid of money or food I was starting off on a hard twelve-mile climb into the upper Harz. After some hours of steady uphill plodding I reached Braunlage, then turned westward on a foot path through the woods until I came out about sundown on the Braunlage Chausee within sight of St. Andreasberg. After the uncertainty of the day and with a gnawing hunger getting the upper hand of me, it was a pleasant sight to see the familiar village a little below me. When, however, I reached the pension and told Frau Garbe of the way I had returned, fourth-class and all, she was scandalized. She had never before had one of her *pensionnaires* travel fourth-class. It was almost a disgrace, fortunate only in that I had not arrived in such a car at the St. Andreasberg station. She then pointed out that I should have telegraphed her from Halle and she would gladly have telegraphed me some money. But then I would have come home in a very commonplace way!

As time went on my ignorance of conversational German gradually diminished. Toward the end of my stay in St. Andreasberg a *Schutzenfest* was held there. It lasted over several days and the competition in various kinds of shooting attracted a considerable crowd. Many side shows were on the outskirts, and in one diminutive tent was said to be a flea-circus. Such an exhibition I had never seen, but as a zoologist I must visit it. Accompanied by a young German school teacher as a guide I made my way to the flea tent and obtained tickets for one of the several afternoon performances. When our turns came, we were seated with some five other visitors around a small white, cloth-covered table, brightly lighted from above and serving as a stage. Three of the party sat next to the table and the other four alternated with the three a little further from the scene of action. All of us had excellent opportunities to view the stage. When the show began the proprietor opened three or four pillboxes filled with cotton and took, by means of delicate forceps, from each box a flea around whose neck was a very fine short wire by which the animal could be handled. Each flea had a very minute white paper skirt about its body. When the flea was picked out of its pillbox it was breathed upon by the showman. It thereupon became warmed and active and when put upon the stage its kicking under its skirts gave it a trembling movement. Three or four such fleas in full activity produced a good imitation of a miniature dance. To an almost microscopic metal wagon two fleas were attached as horses and another as a driver. All were warmed and when put on the slightly sloping stage the kicking of the fleas helped the wagon to glide down the incline. Another flea was put on a thread tightrope and, upside down, crept along it as a tightrope walker. Then the showman's wife was introduced and the fleas were allowed to extract a small amount of nourishment from her plump arm and the show closed. We both agreed that it was well worth the price. I had now had my first experience at a flea-circus.

On our way back to Frau Garbe's the German Fräulein who had been good enough to escort me to the show told me the first German story that I learned to repeat. It was prompted by our experience at the flea-circus. In a small provincial court town the princess of the ruling family wished to visit a flea-circus which had come to the place as part of a local celebration. A private performance was arranged and the princess and her ladies in attendance came at the appointed time. When the show was at its height a very choice flea leaped off the exhibition table toward the princess. The showman was distracted by the possible loss of this best performer and the princess and her ladies withdrew to search for the missing flea. After a long time, they returned in great delight with a handkerchief containing the flea, but on inspection the showman sadly remarked that it was not his flea. This story I could repeat in shattered but understandable German near the end of my St. Andreasberg struggle with the German tongue. At that stage of my linguistic contest I left my pleasant surroundings in the Harz for the University of Leipzig, the winter semester of which opened about the end of September 1891.

XI

German Universities

SOME TO THE STUDIOUS UNIVERSITIES

W. Shakespeare

GERMAN Universities as centers of German learning first made themselves felt in America a little over a century ago. Their type of learning was characterized by unusual thoroughness and exhaustiveness and was somewhat of a novelty in the world of scholarship. Never before had such energy been spent by a body of scholars in the search for truth. It is therefore not surprising that German learning began to attract the attention of scholars of other nationalities. From 1815 when, as Van Wyck Brooks notes, George Tichnor and Edward Everett set out from Boston to become acquainted with the spirit of this new learning, a stream of young American students flowed toward German intellectual centers. Nor did this stream cease till the oncoming of World War I.

In 1891, the year of my going abroad, there were at least a dozen universities in Germany in vigorous activity, and in each of these there was an able, and often a very eminent, teacher and investigator in zoology with his laboratory and his body of workers. So abundant and inviting were the opportunities for study in these universities that the newcomer to Germany was often bewildered in choosing his particular school for study. My foundations in zoology and related subjects had been completed in large part at Harvard, and I therefore felt free to move about in Germany from one center to another rather than spend all my time in one place. I resolved therefore to stay a half-year at each of three universities, Leipzig, Berlin, and Freiburg im Breisgau, all of which were noted as zoological centers. In this way I could become acquainted with the different methods of work and teaching in as many laboratories and under as many heads. When I was about to leave America for Europe, and while the details of my plan of travel were still unsettled, Mr. Alexander Agassiz very kindly gave me a number of personal cards of introduction to foreign zoologists. These proved of great help to me and offered opportunities for acquaintance with a number of zoologists whom I otherwise would not have met. I found, however, contrary to what might have been expected, that most of the older German professors were very friendly in receiving a visiting stranger, even a young one, when they saw that he had a real interest in their institution and its work.

The impressions made upon me on meeting these mature scholars may be conveyed best by a few instances. Such meetings, usually planned, were sometimes unexpectedly accidental. When I was visiting Würzburg, I carried a card of introduction to Professor Carl Semper, whose zoological laboratory was hidden away near one end of the botanical garden. I finally found the laboratory and its director. He showed me some beautiful, capacious vivaria that he had installed, and in one of them a large, spotted salamander which he had brought with him from the United States after his last visit to America. He jokingly introduced me to this salamander as one of the latter's landsmen. He then expressed surprise that I had been able to find his institute and I confessed that I had had some trouble, but I told him that I had been directed to it by the old gardener who, as I pointed out from the window, was still working about in the botanical garden. He looked in the direction I pointed and then laughed and said: "That is not a gardener. That is Professor Julius von Sachs." Thus, without knowing it, I had been talking to probably the most celebrated botanist in Germany at that time. I felt somewhat dismayed, but how was I to know otherwise, for von Sachs was certainly dressed like a gardener. As I was about to leave Professor Semper asked me if I had called on Professor Franz Leydig. I said that I did not know that Professor Leydig was then staying in Würzburg. Professor Semper assured me that he was, gave me his address, and added further that he was certain that Professor Leydig would be glad to receive a call from me. I followed his advice and spent a most enjoyable half-hour with Professor Leydig, for I had worked on several subjects that interested him. Thus, by almost pure accident, I met the "Father of Comparative Histology," a man whose work on the minute structure of the sense-organs in the lower animals had been of greatest importance to me.

On another occasion I was decidedly embarrassed by the kind of greeting given me by one of the older professors. At a luncheon provided for some visiting delegates, at Professor Franz Eilhard Schulze's laboratory in Berlin where I was working, I was introduced to Professor Karl Möbius, whose lectures, as a matter of fact, I was attending. Professor Möbius, who set up in the Berlin zoological museum what was probably the first group of animal wildlife in any such exhibition, was a kindly, rather elderly gentleman, and as we talked together he discovered that I was the author of a small paper on the structure of the rudimentary eyes in the blind crayfishes from Mammoth Cave, Kentucky. He knew the paper, seemed greatly interested in my results, and in congratulating me he took both my hands in his, and without warning impressed a kiss upon my cheek. To me this was a very novel kind of recognition and it took me a moment or two to recover from it. I was told afterwards that in Professor Möbius' homeland such a form of greeting was not at all unusual. As I afterward saw, it was a common practice in southern Europe.

Friendly generosity often marked my association with German professors. When I arrived in Freiburg im Breisgau, I called on Professor Robert Wiedersheim at his residence near the laboratory and presented a card of introduction to him. Before I left, toward the end of my call, he excused himself and presently returned with a small signed photograph of himself. This he kindly gave me with the request that I leave one of mine for him before I departed from Freiburg. Some five months later, when I was about to go to Naples, I called on Professor Wiedersheim to bid him adieu and I then left the photograph that he had requested. Again he excused himself and on returning brought another autographed picture of himself, this time a larger one than the first photograph he had given me, and presented it to me with his best wishes. His generosity evidently exceeded his memory. These reminiscences of German professors and their ways show them a kindly and generous body of men whose very high scholarship had in no way dulled their humanity. But German professors as a group, like all other bodies of men, were not without their black sheep. I was strongly advised not to attempt to call on one professor of zoology because of his surliness, and one whom I did visit was so outrageously egotistical and overbearing that I beat an early retreat. Such individuals were, however, decidedly exceptional, for the great majority of those with whom I came in contact were men of kindly and admirable traits.

What I have said of the older German zoologists was also true of the younger ones. Dr. Otto zur Strassen, who had just taken his doctor's degree under Professor Rudolph Leuckart in Leipzig and who was shortly thereafter made a *privat-docent* in the Leipzig laboratory, introduced me to much of the student life during my first winter in Germany. Dr. zur Strassen was an experienced fencer and did much in training the younger German students in the use of the sword. Dueling was forbidden by German law, but this law was differently interpreted in different parts of the land. In Saxony dueling was under all conditions strictly forbidden, but in Prussia it was allowed as a student recreation as long as it was not a desperate procedure. Consequently, when the Leipzig students wished to carry out a fencing bout they were obliged to move onto Prussian territory. Their method was to go to a nearby town on Prussian, not Saxon ground, and there hold their contests. Dr. zur Strassen was kind enough to take me on one of these excursions and let me see the technique of sword-fencing. The high artist in such a contest was a student who could with his blade draw blood from his opponent's face when and where he liked. It was indeed an artistic kind of butchery and called for very unusual nerve and skill. The German government was said to encourage it as a training for men who were likely to become military officers.

Two other men in the early stages of German university life who were very hospitable and generous to me were Dr. Eugen Korschelt and Dr. Karl Heider, both *privat-docents* in the laboratory of Professor Franz Eilhard Schulze in Berlin. These two men, together with several other young zoologists, made up an informal group that met about once a month for a German supper at some convenient restaurant. They were good enough to invite me and one of my laboratory associates, Dr. W. Frederick Purcell, for an evening's outing with them at a restaurant on the Friedrichstrasse. When we were in the midst of our meal I asked Dr. Korschelt if German children were brought up on *Max and Maurice* as some American youngsters were. He broke into a broad smile and declared that indeed they were and that he even then could repeat most of *Max and Maurice* verbatim. Whereupon he and I began giving, he in German and I in English translation, the inimitable lines of Wilhelm Busch's poem. Thus:

Dr. Korschelt:

> *Wer in Dorfe oder Stadt*
> *Einen Onkel wohnen hat,*
> *Der sei höflich und bescheiden,*
> *Denn das mag der Onkel leiden.—*
> *—Morgens sagt man: "Guten Morgen!*
> *Haben Sie was zu besorgen?"*
> *Bringt ihm, was er haben muss:*
> *Zeitung, Pfeife, Fidibus.*

Parker:

> *If, in village or in town,*
> *You've an uncle settled down,*
> *Always treat him courteously;*
> *Uncle will be pleased thereby.*
> *In the morning: "Morning to you!*
> *Any errand I can do you?"*
> *Fetch whatever he may need—*
> *Pipe to smoke, or news to read.*

And so on in alternate sections till we had finished most of those bad boys' seven tricks. It was a marvelous discovery and united Dr. Korschelt and me, as well as adding to the merriment of those at the supper table. These instances suffice to show that the younger university men in Germany, like their seniors, were in those days friendly and lovable persons.

Although German learning at this time excited on all sides great admiration, it was not without its critics. It was claimed, for instance, that this new learning and its methods induced extreme specialization and excited an interest in minutiae at the expense of general views, that it led in short to knowing more and more about less and less. This criticism was echoed in the American universities where the younger American scholars returning from study in Germany were accused of introducing what was claimed to be a pernicious type of instruction. In zoology the modern laboratory with its microscopes and other instruments was said to be replacing the more wholesome, old-fashioned field work with interests in outdoor natural history. Much of this kind of criticism was to be heard in America, both before I went to Germany and after my return. It was especially voiced to us at Harvard by the chairman of our Visiting Committee for Zoology, Theodore Roosevelt. Mr. Roosevelt condemned unconditionally much of the Harvard teaching in which the microscope was used, and insisted on the establishment in its place of the outdoor study of animals. As a department we heartily endorsed the second part of Mr. Roosevelt's contention, and hoped that he would aid in establishing courses of this kind. The Harvard Corporation was not in a financial situation at that time to increase our budget for this purpose, but we made an effort to raise from other sources funds to enable us to add to our then rather limited curriculum, courses on the natural history of animals in the open field. We called on Mr. Roosevelt to help in the new project, but when this side of the matter was presented to him he never so much as raised a finger. In later years, through other agencies, ample provision for natural history work on animals was installed. Thus, indirectly, Mr. Roosevelt's criticisms yielded fruit.

Some time after this conflict over the kinds of zoology to be taught at Harvard had blown over, a very interesting meeting took place between Mr. Roosevelt and one of our former German exchange professors, Dr. Willy Kükenthal, then of the University of Breslau. Dr. Kükenthal had been a lifelong student of whales and had projected on his own lines an extended study of the development of these unusual mammals. In pursuance of this plan he had spent several years with the whaling fleets in the northern seas, and thus had been able to make a very unusual collection of whale embryos. These as microscopic preparations he had studied with great fullness and had reported his results in numerous publications. In the spring of 1912, when Dr. Kükenthal was at Harvard as exchange professor, he and I were on our way from Washington, where we had been attending a scientific meeting, to Cambridge. Dr. Kükenthal heard that Mr. Roosevelt was in New York at that time and he hoped very much that he could meet so noted a naturalist. I knew a mutual friend who could inform us whether such a meeting could be arranged, and when we arrived in New York from Washington I called up my friend and made inquiry about the matter. He told us that Mr. Roosevelt would shortly be at a given club for luncheon, and that if we would come there after luncheon he felt sure that he could arrange for Dr. Kükenthal to meet Mr. Roosevelt. We went at the appointed time and soon after our arrival we were brought to Mr. Roosevelt. When Dr. Kükenthal was introduced to him and Mr. Roosevelt was told that Dr. Kükenthal was a German exchange professor in zoology at Harvard, Mr. Roosevelt burst out with the statement: "I suppose you work with the microscope!" Dr. Kükenthal with some surprise replied in the affirmative. Whereupon Mr. Roosevelt asked: "And what animals do you study under the microscope?" assuming presumably that they must be some insignificantly, small creatures. To this interrogation Dr. Kükenthal quite truthfully replied: "Whales." I had seen Mr. Roosevelt under many circumstances and had recognized his great ability to meet any emergency in which he found himself, but I never saw him so completely nonplused as he was at that moment by Dr. Kükenthal's reply, nor did he recover himself during the whole of the ensuing, brief conversation. This ended, we expressed our appreciation of the opportunity of having met Mr. Roosevelt and left. Dr. Kükenthal was pleased with his brief interview with Mr. Roosevelt, but had noticed his slight discomfiture during the conversation and asked me if he, Dr. Kükenthal, had made any remark that was improper. I assured him that nothing which he had said could be so construed, though I did not tell him of Mr. Roosevelt's antipathy to microscopes, nor of my suspicion that Mr. Roosevelt was still puzzling over the question of how a whale could be made the object of microscopic study. Thus the old problem of field work and of microscopic work in zoology got a new setting, but not till long after Mr. Roosevelt had ceased to be a member of the Harvard Visiting Committee for Zoology.

The contrast between these early days and the present, especially in Germany, calls for some comment. In the early eighteen-nineties there was much talk in German academic circles of the absence among the younger university men of individuals of the first quality to take the places of the distinguished men of the older generation who were withdrawing from service. It did seem true that the period of great academic personalities was passing. Could there be a natural rhythm in such matters and was German academic life, and perhaps the life of the nation as a whole, entering a period of depression? Or were the best minds in Germany being tempted to other lands by offers of increased facilities? There certainly was more or less emigration on the part of German scholars. The threat of anti-semitism, which was certainly rising in Germany at that time, might well have influenced university men to leave that land; either because of fear of persecution or because of their disapproval of the general attitude of Germany in such matters. The question thus appeared to be a complex one with many sides to it. That there was a real problem involved seemed to be beyond doubt.

Then came the First World War, in which the German universities, already showing evidence of internal decline, suffered together with the universities of all other lands. The enormous and profound social wreckage which resulted from that war is impossible to picture, and yet it was followed in many ways by encouraging evidences of renewed vitality.

The generous, kindly Germany of my student days is in the strongest possible contrast with the present Germany, as different as day is from night. Yet it seems impossible that in one short generation a whole nation could be so transformed as Nazi Germany seems to have been. Undoubtedly the political situation has played no small part in all these alterations. Some years ago I had a lengthy visit from an old friend of mine who had attained high standing in German affairs, university and even national. At that time the Nazi regime was beginning to make itself strongly felt, though war was by no means on the horizon as yet. I knew that my friend's situation was a critical one, for I had heard him express his opinions at a much earlier time, but I resolved to say nothing to him about politics unless he, himself, chose to open up such matters. For several weeks the subject was not mentioned by either of us. Finally my friend found occasion to say something on the matter, and I then frankly spoke my mind to him. I soon found that his views were what I had suspected they might be, and he summed up our conversation by what seemed to me a very sound declaration. He told me how immeasurably sad it made him feel to find that the control of his homeland had passed into the hands of ignorant men.

We know that a form of government which rests upon might to the exclusion of human rights cannot be allowed to prevail. After such a regime as the Nazis set up the recovery of Germany, in my opinion, will depend much upon the number of Germans who can see the situation more or less as my old friend did. The German government must be taken from the hands of ignorant men. This step will give to Germany a chance for a renewed life and with the return of its people to national sanity there will spring up again, in my opinion, that form of intellectual environment in which universities can flourish.

XII

Italy in Springtime

KENNST DU DAS LAND, WO DIE ZITRONEN BLÜHN,
IM DUNKELN LAUB DIE GOLD-ORANGEN GLÜHN,
EIN SANFTER WIND VOM BLAUEN HIMMEL WEHT,
DIE MYRTE STILL UND HOCH DER LORBEER STEHT,
KENNST DU ES WOHL?

Goethe

VEDI NAPOLI E POI MORI!

EVERY young zoologist of my generation was desirous, as a part of his early training, to work at the Naples Zoological Station. Through a request from Professor Robert Wiedersheim I received an appointment to a table at this noted station for the first half of 1893. The appointment was in large measure due to the generosity of the director of the station, Professor Anton Dohrn, to whom I owe my sincere thanks. I left Freiburg im Breisgau for Naples early in January 1893 and entered Switzerland at Basel. Here in the railroad station, an old *Gepäckträger* asked me if I wished him to speak "Deech-deech" or "Sweetzer-deech." I requested "Deech-deech" and inquired of him how he had learned the language. He said he had spent two days at Mulhause in Alsace and that he had found "Deech-deech" very easy to pick up. When I thought of my years of struggle to attain even my small amount of conversational German I was fully persuaded that foreign languages were not my forte. From Basel I went directly to Zurich where I called upon Dr. Arnold Lang, then professor of zoology at the university, a former associate of the Naples station. On learning that I was on my way to Naples he congratulated me, for, he declared, there was nothing so beautiful as spring in Italy. From Zurich I went by train along the lake, through the ice and snow of Switzerland, and then up by means of the marvelous system of spiral tunnels to the great St. Gotthard tunnel from which, after some twenty minutes of travel, we came out into the Ticino valley. And what a transformation that twenty minutes made! At the northern entrance to the St. Gotthard we were in the snows and ice of wintry German Switzerland. At its southern exit we suddenly emerged into the sunny spring of the Italian-Swiss countryside.

To one hungry for sunshine and blue skies nothing could have been more striking than this immediate burst into the bright, early spring of the Ticino. It was Sunday and the church bells of the little villages nestling on the sides of the valley sent out a peal of welcome in their thousand-toned chimes. If this was not Italy itself, it was surely a foretaste of that land of beauty. Soon we had dropped down into Bellinzona, then Chiasso, the Italian frontier, and finally at nightfall to the town of Como. The next morning I went by a small steamer up the lake to Bellagio and then by afternoon boat back again to Como. In the intense sunlight of a perfectly blue sky the surrounding mountains, snow-covered above and dotted here and there with villas below, made a perfect setting for the reflecting blue waters of Como. Such a day is not soon forgotten!

By evening train I traveled from Como to Milan, and here I stopped over a day to climb about the cathedral pinnacles and to see Leonardo's "Last Supper." Then, again by train, to Genoa where I made a brief halt before I took a boat for Naples.

The gentleman who sat at meals with me on shipboard spoke no English and I no Italian. He, however, was adept in sign language and by this means we mutually made ourselves understood. When my companion had enough of anything I noticed that he said to the steward "Basta, basta," and thus I began to learn Italian. After two days aboard ship we steamed by Ischia and Capri into what is to me the most interesting and perhaps the most beautiful bay in the world. To the east rose Vesuvius with snow skirting its crater and with occasional bursts of dark vapor from its summit. Stretching along the whole curve of the northern shore of the bay was a succession of little towns merging finally at the center in the great panorama of Naples itself, overtopped by St. Elmo. Soon the steamer drew up near the docks and by small boats we and our luggage were landed. Those who come to the Naples zoological station are usually furnished with detailed information about what they should do either at the railroad station or at the docks. As our boat came into port I could see on the water front of the city, in a park-like enclosure, the building of the zoological station. Hence, I knew the direction in which I should go. I had my bag with me, jumped at once into a *carricello,* and shouted to the driver, as my printed directions told me, "Aquario." He started on a very different course from what I would have taken and again I shouted "Aquario," but he continued on his way. He drove me for fully an hour and a half up towards St. Elmo and all over that part of the city giving me a most interesting view of the surroundings and finally, after a long detour, he brought me to the aquarium. I knew by the directions given me that his fare should be eighty-five centesimi and to include a *pourboire* I handed him a lire, one hundred centesimi. He sprung into the air like a jumping jack and demanded, so far as I could make out, ten lire, two hands up with all his ten fingers spread. I stood my ground and gave him nothing more. I might have shouted "Basta, basta" had I had my wits about me, but I had not. In the course of the commotion, which had drawn quite a crowd about us, a door-tender from the aquarium came out. To my relief I found he could speak German and I explained to him what I had done and what had been done to me. He told me, what I felt was surely the case, that the driver had taken me on an unwarranted ride with the intention of collecting a large fee, and that I should go into the station and he would attend to the owner of the *carricello.* Some time later, when all had quieted down, I came back to the door-tender and asked him how he had come out of the affair and whether I owed him any money. He told me that he had sent the driver packing for having tried to impose upon me and that what I had given the driver was the correct amount. Thus I had my first lesson in Neapolitan street life. In this particular affair I confess I felt a certain compunction, for the driver of the *carricello* had really given me a very interesting ride. But, as I was afterward told at the station, such attempts at extortion ought never to be countenanced in any way.

Neapolitan life, such as the stranger meets with on the streets and in the shops of the town, must be learned by experience. I found that at the Naples station the older workers were very willing to help the new ones in learning the ropes, so to speak, and that these in turn were supposed to help those who were still less experienced. Almost immediately on my arrival in Naples I found I must buy a new toothbrush. One of the more experienced of the younger men, Dr. Victor Willem, came to my aid and proposed that we go together to make the purchase. He took me to an apothecary's shop not far from the station, in the window of which hung a large sign *Pressi Fissi,* fixed prices. This seemed very favorable. We were shown a large tray divided into compartments with different kinds of toothbrushes at various prices. I was choosing a brush from the eighty centesimi section, and was about to take it and pay for it when Willem intervened, put the brush back in its place and talked with me about its quality and so forth. There then ensued much further conversation with the proprietor about brushes in general, during which I noticed that Willem took the brush I had chosen, looked at it, and then put it back in, I believe, the sixty centesimi compartment. After a while he picked it out again, handed it to the apothecary and intimated that we would take it. But the apothecary returned the brush to the eighty section. Then followed more friendly conversation while Willem slipped the brush into the seventy section. From this he eventually extracted it and we finally bought it at that price. With kindly and considerate words the proprietor showed us out of his shop with the request that we call on him again. Thus I began to understand what *pressi fissi* meant and how one bought and sold in Naples. To go into a shop as we do at home and with as few words as possible request, pay for, and take away a desired article would have been in Naples the height of rudeness. Purchasing in this town was a social function and was to be done with due consideration to the amenities of life. During this intercourse articles and prices are without great show adjusted, but the main thing is that a friendly intercommunication is maintained and that the purchaser and seller finally part with expressions of mutual esteem and good will.

American life will perhaps never adapt itself to this form of bargaining, but this does not prove that American life may not have something to learn in this respect. I once had the misfortune to go uninstructed into a barbershop in Naples, and when the barber had finished with me I was in the embarrassing position of not knowing what I should pay. The barber would merely say "What the gentleman wishes to give," and there I was caught hard and fast. In the end I gave the barber a lire, but when I returned to the station I was told it should have been eighty centesimi. All my friends laughed at me for having been such an ignoramus and I dare say that the barber did likewise, though surely up his sleeve.

The atmosphere of the station was in every sense paternal. I was taken by a station official to several addresses for rooms within easy walking distance of the aquarium, and I finally arranged for breakfast and room with a Swiss family half a mile off. Hither, my belongings, which I had addressed to the station, were sent and I found myself quickly and comfortably settled for the season. Most of the members of this Swiss family spoke German so that I had no difficulties with the language. At the station a group of the younger workers under the guidance of Dr. Hugo Eisig took their midday meal together at Nicolo's Sereno Restaurant, a miniature eating place situated a short distance above the Villa Nazionale where the station stood, and in the direction of St. Elmo. Old Nicolo was a cadaverous-looking Italian who did all the duties in the restaurant except cooking. He appeared to live in deadly fear of Dr. Eisig who, as a matter of fact, brought most of the custom to Nicolo's small place. Nicolo would sell to each of us for ninety lires a strip of tickets that entitled the purchaser to midday meals for a month, at the end of which time each of us gave Nicolo ten lires additional as a *pourboire* and then began the operation over again. Our midday meal, *collazione,* came at eleven o'clock. On arrival at our family table each received a large section of Roman lettuce which was then sliced, mixed with lemon juice and salt, and set aside to soften as a salad. Then followed a heaping plate of spaghetti, with tomato or some other sauce, and while this was being served and eaten the fish dealer or the butcher from a neighboring shop would bring in a large platter of fresh fish or meat from which each one chose an item to be turned over to the restaurant cook for preparation. This was then served with some appropriate vegetables and the meal was concluded with our salad, some fruit, usually a fresh fig or an orange, and a demitasse of Italian black coffee. Red table wine, Posilipo Vecchio, was extra and came in a small bottle, a quinto, for each person. It was commonly taken diluted with seltzer water from a siphon on the table. On particular days it was usual to celebrate by concluding our meal with a glass of Marsala or other special wine.

The Sereno was frequented by a number of patrons other than those who came from the station. One of these, a Neapolitan lady, of noble blood we were told but evidently in reduced circumstances, sat usually not far from us. In all the time I was there I never heard her utter a word. We were informed that she was above speaking to others in the restaurant. Her communications in ordering her meal from poor Nicolo, who hovered around her like a condemned sinner, were always by signs. He would mention in a very subdued voice an available dish that he thought might appeal to her appetite, whereupon she would in due time wave her hand under her chin which meant never mention that again, emphatically never. Or she would raise her little finger for a moment to indicate that she would perhaps take a half-portion. By such vague indications Nicolo would gather some idea of what she would probably accept, though despair would seize him if he misinterpreted her motions. We were told that she spent as little as possible at the restaurant that she might be seen once a week riding in a *carricello* on the Corso. Two or three elderly gentlemen also came to the Sereno for their meals, but of these no special comments ever reached us. Such was the family to which poor Nicolo catered.

The lower floor of the station was occupied by a large, public aquarium, hence the popular name of the place, the aquario. Above this were the laboratories, the library, and the administrative offices. Each worker had a small cubicle by himself with an aquarium and running sea water. Here he was provided with living material as needed, and here he worked unrestrained and with all necessary facilities. Having settled myself in my quarters I paid my respects to the director, Dr. Dohrn, and soon afterwards met his worthy assistants, Dr. Paul Mayer and Dr. Wilhelm Giesbrecht.

Into all these arrangements any newcomer to the station quickly slipped, if he so chose, and thus he found himself almost at once at home. The group at the Sereno formed a natural one for outings in the neighborhood of Naples, and few Sundays went by that we did not visit interesting places in the Neapolitan countryside. Our group was made up of men of several nationalities. Predominantly German it included two Englishmen, one Spaniard, one Dutchman, three Belgians, one of whom, Dr. Victor Willem, was in a way appointed to care for me. We foreigners all chattered German of more or less purity. Difficulties with our Italian environment were always adjusted by Dr. Eisig who knew the Neapolitan even better, perhaps, than the Neapolitan knew himself. Thus we were protected from a world of wildness and disorder in Naples itself and yet free to plunge into it at any time we wished.

We worked in the station until about four in the afternoon. Thereupon several of us, particularly Willem and I, would take a walk into one of the more inviting parts of the town or the country. A favorite direction was up on the Posilipo, a ridge extending southwestward toward the open sea and with a wonderful drive on its crest from which there were superb views outward over the bay to Vesuvius and backward over the town. Everyone in Naples watches Vesuvius for its daily changes in mood and temper. It is the fear and joy of the region. Shortly after my arrival in Naples new taxes were imposed on salt and on tobacco; in consequence even Vesuvius was said to have cut down on smoking.

The climb from the station to the ridge of the Posilipo was by an unfrequented path that led past an ancient tomb reputed to be that of Virgil. Little did I think as I slaved over the *Aeneid* in school that the time would come when I should find a favorite walk near the supposed burial place of the author of this immortal poem. The path at its upper end opened through a low stone wall to the main thoroughfare, and here on the wall almost always was to be found an aged Italian with his basket of oranges. Each orange had been cut from the tree with a leaf attached to its stem to show its freshness. The common price of the fruit was two for a soldo, but the great event was to get three for that sum. The procedure was to lay down a copper soldo on the wall next to the old man and then with a mild flow of conversation to select the fruit. Anyone could pick out two oranges and walk away, but the supreme effort was to get three in your hand, they were of the small Italian variety, and then joking and cajoling with the old fellow to back slowly away with the three oranges. If, in the slow backward retreat, the purchaser could reach a distance of six or eight feet from the seller while in animated conversation, the old man would smile weakly and submissively and the oranges belonged to the purchaser. If, on the other hand, the seller's face stiffened a little, you were in honor bound to return an orange. This of course we always did, for otherwise it would have been theft. Many a time we played this game above the tomb of Virgil, and sometimes our old friend won and sometimes we did. What went through his head when with his resigned, sad smile he succumbed in the bargaining I do not know, but I suspect he may have said to himself "I did not make the oranges! The good God made them. What right have I to withhold them?"

As we walked out on the main road of the Posilipo with the beautiful bay of Naples to the left and to the right Pozzuoli and its exquisite shore line reaching to Cape Misenum, it seemed like an enchanted landscape, one that no art could improve. Sooner or later we would turn to the left, go down some flights of worn tufa steps to the lower road next to the bay, and then take our way back towards Naples. At a number of places on this road were the fountains of the pure Sereno water where neighbors drew their household supplies. As we retraced our steps toward town we would meet groups of women and girls carrying away from these public water-supplies large buckets, almost tubs, of water for home use. Each woman wore on her head a thick pad of cloth on which the tub rested, balanced there by one hand. The water and tub together were of very considerable weight and the transport was a feat that called for unusual skill, for it was done without spilling. I called Willem's attention to a particular young woman who, with marvelous form and adroitness, was slowly ascending a stone stairway with a more than heavy tub on her head. She reminded me of one of the caryatids from the Athenian Acropolis, so straight, so well-poised she was. In some way quite unsuspected by us, she sensed our interest and, though at a distance of a hundred steps or more she turned, faced us, and with body and tub of water perfectly motionless, she shot forth a volume of language the chief merit of which for me was that I did not understand it. Then wheeling slowly where she stood, she gradually and laboriously continued her ascent. We were not in the least uncomplimentary in our quiet talk about her nor did we suspect that she knew of our distant presence, but she certainly made us feel that she would have none of us. This encounter was exceptional on the Posilipo where, as a rule, our walks carried us through a countryside of semi-tropical peace and quiet.

XIII

Italy (concluded)

OPEN MY HEART, AND YOU WILL SEE
GRAVED INSIDE OF IT "ITALY."

R. Browning

THE living sea animals that we used in the laboratory were collected for us in the Bay of Naples and the neighboring waters by a corps of station fishermen under the leadership of Signor Lo Bianco. Salvatore Lo Bianco was from the African shore, a man of superb physique and tremendous energy. What he did not know of the marine life about Naples was not worth knowing. He had charge of the small, collecting steamer belonging to the station, the *Johannes Müller*. She went out almost every day on a collecting trip and those of us in the laboratory were often invited. As I was walking through the Villa early one morning on my way to the station I heard my name called from the water-side and looking in that direction I saw Lo Bianco waving his hand to me and intimating that the *Johannes Müller* was about to leave. It took very little to entice me on board, where I found several of our party including Victor Willem and soon we were off. The trip was to the neighborhood of Capri. The bay was rough and I soon began to feel a little squeamish. Lo Bianco, who always spoke German with us, asked me in that tongue if I had beetles in my stomach, *Käfer im Magen,* to which I assented. He then went forward and brought back with him a large female sea urchin and a big piece of Italian bread. He cut the urchin open and told me to dip bits of bread into the ovaries and eat them as the Neapolitans did. I followed his advice and when my stomach had something to work on I made a full recovery. Meanwhile the whole expedition fell to singing—"Solo mio," "Funiculi, funicula," and the like. Then Lo Bianco turned to me and said that some years ago Dr. William Patton, at that time in the station, taught them an American song which soon became very popular, but which unfortunately had been forgotten. Would I be good enough to sing some American songs to see if by chance they could recover Patton's melody? I was obliged to confess that I could not sing, but I proposed to whistle hoping in that way to recover the air. After attempts in many directions I at last hit upon the tune of "John Brown's Body" whereat Lo Bianco shouted with glee. In short order "John Brown's Body" was resurrected, for the words were now easily recalled.

We landed on Capri at the Marina Grande and Lo Bianco quickly had us in small boats to be rowed to the Blue Grotto, while the *Johannes Müller* went off on her collecting trip. Since we came from the zoological station we were passed into and out of the grotto with some ceremony and no charge. It was a very favorable day for the expedition. The remarkable reflection of the blue light of the sky from the white sand under the sea water that fills the lower portion of the grotto gives all objects inside this rocky chamber a strange, uncanny tint. We had a strikingly good exhibition of this weird effect. From the grotto we came back by boat to the Marina Grande and were there told that we could wander about the island till well into the afternoon. Willem and I went to a small restaurant on the way to Timberio where we had spaghetti and a bottle of Capri bianco. Wine usually has very little effect upon me, but this white wine of Capri so worked upon me that when we set out for our afternoon walk the whole island seemed many times more beautiful than before. We climbed to Timberio, the remains of the Villa of Tiberius where that Roman emperor spent his last years. From the heights of Timberio we took in the superb panorama of the incomparable bay and its surroundings, with Vesuvius towering above everything else. We had ample time to climb about on the tawny cliffs with the deep-blue sea in constant motion below us. Then we wandered slowly down to the dock where we were picked up by the *Johannes Müller* and brought back to Naples after a day the like of which would be hard to equal and which, so far as I was concerned, resulted from my coming to the station that morning a quarter of an hour earlier than usual.

Capri as a sea trip is equaled only by Vesuvius as a land trip. Vesuvius, like any real Neapolitan, is strangely temperamental and it is well to get acquainted with the volcano in his different moods. There are three times when he should be visited, in full action, in full quiescence, and when he is puffing a vapor cloud once every ten minutes or so. For a trip to Vesuvius, which calls for a whole day, we went by horsecar from Naples along the bay to the town of Portici. Here provisions were bought for the trip: a good supply of Italian bread, Swiss cheese, oranges and, on the road to the volcano, a bottle or so of Lachryma Christi. This wine we always bought from an old hermit who lived in a hut well up the road toward the cone. In the square at Portici a few guides commonly met us to offer their services. We pretended to misunderstand their requests and to suppose that they were the ones who wished to be guided up the volcano, and we all fell to offering our services to them till the villagers standing about saw the joke and made so much fun of the real guides that they finally beat a retreat. Freed of the rabble we walked up the carriage road and made our way past the volcano observatory to the base of the cinder cone. Over a zigzag footpath, now and then obliterated, we slowly climbed for about an hour and a half up the steep sides of the cone to reach the top about noon. And then what a sight, the whole Neapolitan region at our feet! Seaward the bay of Naples in all its glory, bounded by Ischia to the west and Capri to the south, and over the peninsula of Sorrento the Gulf of Salerno. Landward the broad fertile countryside behind Naples ending on the horizon in the Neapolitan Apennines. And, if you are on the windward side of the crater, what an air for clearness and purity; to the other side sulphurous fumes. At the top we usually took our meal, consuming much of our bread and Swiss cheese moistened with orange juice and Lachryma Christi. If the volcano was absolutely quiet you could go to the edge of the crater and look into a deep rock-walled pit ending in a funnel of loose gravel and rock, a harmless, lifeless depth. If the volcano was in occasional action the bottom of this pit would begin from time to time to oscillate, vapor would break through, and then suddenly with an enormous explosion the whole bottom of sand, gravel, and stone would rise with the vapor and shoot like a gigantic cannon-burst far up into the air above the cone. The vapor would float off on the wind and the sand, stone, and rocks thrown up by the explosion would fall back, mostly into the crater down the sides of which it would rattle, or be carried off a short distance by the wind and dropped on the sides of the cone. Hence it would be well under these circumstances to approach the crater from the windward side. Presently all would be quiet again and the pit might be visible to its very bottom. When the volcano was in full action explosion would follow explosion accentuated by flashes of light. Because of the continuous shower of stones and rocks it was commonly not possible under such conditions to reach the edge of the crater in safety. These are some of the moods of Vesuvius. They seem to come and go as the mountain listeth. It is not surprising that the ordinary Neapolitan looks on the volcano as a living thing. The descent of the cinder cone, the ascent of which costs on foot an hour and a half of hard climbing, can be made in the astoundingly short time of about two minutes. One gigantic stride after another in the loose springy, cinder slope will bring any sure-footed pedestrian in an unbelievably brief interval to the bottom of the cone. But avoid falling! Around from the cinder cone a path leads to the Atrio del Cavallo where, in 1893, through a rift in the side of the volcano a slow, steady flow of molten lava was oozing out. Here a copper soldo piece could be stuck into the doughy lava and after the lava had cooled coin and lava could be broken off and carried away as a souvenir. If it was cold on the top of the cone, here next the flowing lava it was hot enough.

To go to Pompeii, which was to the southeast of Vesuvius, we took the train at Naples, passed between the volcano and the bay, and stopped off at the little station for the buried town. Here were the marvelously complete remains of a place of the first century of our era brought to light simply by the removal of the ash that had been thrown out by the first eruption of Vesuvius. To wander about in its empty streets gives a sense of Latin antiquity not to be gained in any other way. The Roman forum is a disclosure of layer upon layer of the past, but Pompeii is a town caught and preserved in one day, a marvelous snapshot of its existence. At the little theater the stone seats were numbered with Roman numerals; we were amused to find that five of us, by no means especially large persons, could not crowd on fewer than six seats. The Pompeians, and others of their race, were small people. But Pompeii is to be seen and studied to be enjoyed. Not far from it, to the south near where Castellammare now stands, was ancient Stabiae suffocated by the same rain of ashes which buried Pompeii. Here the great Roman naturalist Pliny the elder lost his life during the first eruption in 79 A.D. As a Roman official he came from across the bay to help distressed Roman citizens, and as a naturalist he wished to learn the nature of a volcanic eruption. The first day that I spent in Italy I saw Pliny's birthplace, Como, and now here not far from Vesuvius I was close to where he died.

Just outside Pompeii, at a restaurant kept by a kindly Swiss, we took our afternoon meal. As we sat round his hospitable board we conversed in German, as was our wont. Some one of the party then asked the host if he could name our nationalities, for it was plain that we were not all Germans. He was remarkably successful in his efforts till he came to me when he said "Norddeutscher." I was amazed, first, that our host should recognize by my speech the part of Germany in which I had learned conversational German, and next that he should mistake me for a member of that race. It is true that after the length of time that I had been abroad I had learned to speak German fairly well, but I never supposed that any one, not even a German-Swiss, would take me for a real German. Such, however, was his guess.

Not all the strangers who visit Naples visit Camaldoli, but that is their misfortune. Of all the entrancing views in this region of such views Camaldoli has the most entrancing of all. The monastery of Camaldoli is some four miles northwest of Naples and on the highest land near the city. Its garden seems to include within its outward scope every spot of interest and of beauty in the whole Neapolitan region. Everything worth while about Naples, the bay and its islands, the surrounding sea from Cumae in the west to Sorrento in the south, and all the ancient craters, Solfatara, Astroni, and the like, are spread out before the visitor. The Camaldolites were an order of great austerity, but they knew as few others did, how and where to feast the eye on the beauties of nature. A knock at the monastery garden gate will bring a monk, who, for a small fee, will show the visitor to a pleasant seat in the garden and fetch him a bottle of wine. There in the late afternoon light the whole Neapolitan landscape becomes a dream and the visitor finds it hard to tear himself away before sundown.

Once when we had made our way to Camaldoli and sought admission we were told at the gate that the garden was closed for a short time. The Prince of Naples who had just married had received permission from the Pope to bring his bride to the garden for the view. The father added that if we would wait a short time outside till the couple had departed we could be admitted. So we sat on the stone wall next the road and awaited the pleasure of the Prince. Presently the gate opened and he and his lady came through. We all rose, took off our hats, and stood in silence. This seemed to me rather ungracious and so I stepped up and spoke to the Prince in English, regretting that I could not speak in Italian. I expressed our wish that he and his wife had found the view from the garden all that they had expected and I complimented him on being the Prince of a region with such natural beauty. He replied at once in excellent English and expressed their pleasure at what they had seen and said that they were sorry to have kept us waiting. Then we all bowed and the royal couple departed by carriage. Was I overbold? No, I was simply American and the Prince was democratic enough to accept me as such. As everyone knows, he subsequently became King Victor Emmanuel. He is the only royal personage with whom I have ever conversed.

During much of the spring we had talked of a walk around the Gulf of Salerno, a walk that would take perhaps a week or so and which would include Paestum, Salerno, Amalfi, and Sorrento. At last the party was made up and it was planned to start from Naples about the first of June. On the appointed morning I went to the railroad station in a tremendous downpour of rain and found no one of the party there except Victor Willem. He and I debated the project and the weather and finally resolved to go. As the train passed Torre del Greco the sun broke out and the day could not have turned finer and clearer. At Salerno we changed to a local train and well before noon we arrived at Paestum. We had been told that the region was malarial and that we should not visit it early or late in the day nor lie in the grass. At that time the mosquito was not known to be the vector of the fever. It is remarkable, however, how well the precautions given us fitted the situation. As everyone knows, Paestum was a Greek town of great antiquity, having been founded about 600 B.C., and its three temples are among the finest examples of Greek architecture still extant. This is particularly true of the so-called Temple of Neptune, a Doric structure in an unusually fine state of preservation. During my sojourn in Italy I had become accustomed to almost daily contacts with the material evidences of Roman antiquity, but to come across the remains of a far more ancient settlement such as Paestum was before it became Paestum was a real revelation. Little is left of this ancient Greek town but its walls and its temples. It was indeed a step farther back than I had thus far gone in the ancient history of Europe, and as a memorial of these very early times the Temple of Neptune in its perfect proportions and its exquisite simplicity stood out as an emblem of the solidarity of all that was best in the Greek way of life. With real regret we left this memorable spot and betook ourselves to the afternoon train for Salerno.

At Salerno we had an early repast and after resting a while we started on our extended walk along the shore road to Amalfi. The distance was over twelve miles. As we left Salerno we were accompanied by several *carricello* drivers who, when they heard that we intended to walk to Amalfi, declared the proposal impossible. We told them, however, that we knew the distance, were good walkers, and expected to reach Amalfi before ten o'clock. It was a superbly clear evening after the rain, and as the darkness gathered, the moonlight was all that could be wished. We had allowed ourselves ample time and we took the road at an easy pace. Vietri, Majori, Atrani were passed and finally somewhat before nine we reached Amalfi. As we entered the town we were surprised to be met by several hotel keepers who recommended their places for overnight in highest terms, but we told them that we were going to the Cappuccini, the well-known monastery above the main road. We climbed the flight of steps leading from the road to the Capuchin establishment where, after finding one of the monks, we were given sleeping quarters. Up early the next morning we took breakfast on the veranda with its fascinating pergola and view over the cliffs, the little harbor, and across the waters of the gulf shifting in colors with the morning sunlight. After breakfast we arranged to leave our packs at the monastery, and to keep our rooms for another night. We then sauntered down into Amalfi, to its cathedral, and finally to its harbor. As the morning wore on we walked up the valley behind the town, then back along the shore, reversing our direction of the night before, till we came to the road for Ravello. Up this we made our way to the town itself. Ravello, with its evidences of the Saracenic invasion, was even more interesting than Amalfi. Thence, after *collazione* and a brief siesta, we turned back to Amalfi and the Cappuccini where we spent the late afternoon enjoying the sights of the town and the view.

The next morning we called for our bill, but found it difficult to get one. We were told by the fathers that the season had really not yet opened and that they were very glad to give us lodgings and help us on our way. Eventually we succeeded in paying a very small part of what we thought we owed. For some three days we continued our walk along this indescribable coast line, now on the main drive and now on footpaths, stopping overnight at such villages as Prajano and Positano where we were received with great hospitality and where, as at the Cappuccini, we had difficulty in getting bills. Finally we made our last stop at Sorrento. Here we stayed a day or so to enjoy the wonders of the place and to rest a little before our return to Naples. We walked out on the road to Massalubrense with its grand views of the sea and of Capri. When we came to leave our stopping place at Sorrento we again had difficulty in getting a bill. Our host had lived in New York some fifteen years and spoke English perfectly well. I therefore asked him why we had had such trouble after leaving Salerno in getting our hotel bills. He smiled and said: "You are both well known along the whole shore from Salerno to Sorrento. We have all been informed of your coming. You and your friend each carry a Baedeker's guidebook to southern Italy. You are from the Naples zoological station. This guide book is edited for south Italy, from that station. Are you not preparing a new edition? We hotel keepers were told so and we want to stand well in this new issue. We are more than glad to have you as our guests and we should be pleased to keep you at our establishments much longer than you seem willing to stay, and without charge." A sudden light burst in upon me and I told our host we should do all we could for him, but that we could promise nothing more than the truth. We then took a *carricello* for Castellammare. In the *carricello* I told Willem of the fraud we had been practicing unconsciously on the innkeepers from Salerno to Sorrento. He agreed with me that it was the first time that we, as strangers, had ever really beaten Italians. I confess that I felt a little ashamed of the whole affair, much as I did about the small fee paid to the driver of the *carricello* on my first day in Naples. However, there seemed to be nothing for us to do but to accept unreservedly what Fate had given us. Sunburned and happy we returned from Castellammare by train to Naples and to the zoological station. Our comrades, who had been frightened off by the weather, heard our tale with some incredulity, especially in the matter of our hotel bills, but after much quizzing they admitted that we were probably telling the truth and that the laugh was on them.

It was June. Spring in Italy, 1893, was over and after having had a season of supreme enjoyment and intense interest I began with regrets to make my plans for a departure northward. More than ever did I now appreciate Dr. Lang's declaration that of all places to spend the opening half of the year Naples stood at the forefront.

XIV

Homeward Bound

AS HOME HIS FOOTSTEPS HE HATH TURN'D
FROM WANDERING ON A FOREIGN STRAND.

W. Scott

THE Naples zoological station, paternal to the end, packed my trunk, sealed it so that it might leave Italy without the inspection of its contents, and sent it to Rotterdam whence I planned to sail for America in August. I bade my many friends at the station regretful adieus and took train for Rome. It was early summer and the weather was turning warm, so I traveled with light hand luggage. The Naples station had provided me with what proved to be an excellent hotel address in Rome, and there I remained a week or more seeing the endless sights of this eternal city. In the restaurant of the hotel I fell to using the hand language which I had learned at the Sereno in Naples. I noticed that the waiter seemed amused. Finally in a friendly way he asked me if I had stayed in Naples some time and suggested that my signs were Neapolitan. He further intimated, in a most considerate manner, that the sign language of Naples outside that southern region was on the whole infra dig, and was not used by experienced travelers. I thanked him for the suggestion and from that time on I limited myself to my small Italian vocabulary.

In Rome I certainly played the tourist. With Baedeker in hand I literally did the town. From the Lupercal, where the she-wolf cared for Romulus and Remus, to the latest improvements on the Tiber embankments I saw all, and as a conscientious tourist I checked off the items in my guidebook. To this volume of Baedeker I refer the inquisitive reader for the sights of Rome. They are far too numerous even to be listed here. The Roman Forum, the Colosseum, the Triumphal Arches, the Appian Way over which all Rome had marched, the Cloaca Maxima, these and a thousand other relics in this ancient city were all duly visited. I stood by the Apollo Belvedere and thought of the German who had himself photographed next this statue and then on the post card picture thus taken wrote to his wife "Links der Apollo, rechts ich." I went in proper spirit to the Vatican, the Sistine Chapel, St. Peter's, and I also visited the picture galleries, the Palaces, and countless other places. As I was trying one day to find the Rospigliosi Palace, for a sight of Guido Reni's "Aurora," I met a young man, who, in broken Italian, asked me the way to this very place. The clothes I had on, as well as my shoes, were Neapolitan-made so that I could not blame my questioner for speaking to me in the tongue of the land; but in reply I tried English, at which he laughed, and together we then ferreted out on the map the way to the Rospigliosi. As we walked along toward our common destination and chatted he told me that he came from a small town in Massachusetts, Newton by name, whereupon I confessed that I, too, came from an equally small place, Cambridge, Massachusetts, across the Charles River from Newton. At this juncture we formed a partnership and together went to all such places, as for instance, the Catacombs, where for personal safety, according to Baedeker, parties of not fewer than two should go. Thus I indulged in a perfect glut of sight-seeing such as I had never experienced before and such as, I trust, I may never subject myself to again. In a remote way, in the back of my head, there lurked a reminiscence of what Mark Twain in his innocence had done when in foreign lands, and it seemed to me that I must surely do no less. At times I was reduced to what I once saw in a small picture gallery in the Netherlands. I was sitting almost alone in a part of the gallery where there were some paintings that I much enjoyed when in came a professional guide chartered evidently to escort a single file of "school-marms" through the gallery and show them the best in the least possible time. As he passed he pointed to a portrait hanging on the wall and said with great distinctness "Holbein, Holbein, Holbein" and then dashed onward. By that time the rear of the line had reached me and one young woman with pencil and note-book in hand asked of another immediately in front of her "Oh! What did he say? What *did* he say?" to which the one who had a a better position for hearing replied "I don't know. He spoke in German." Thus, too, was I rushed through Rome, the eternal. Being on my way home my American temper which had been in a state of torpidity now for full two years began to reassert itself. I, too, must do things quickly and to the point.

In a state near exhaustion but enormously edified, I left Rome by train for Florence. Each day the sun had been growing stronger and warmer so that the shady side of the way was the more comfortable. I was still in Italy. Hence I resolved to throw off this Roman fever and to bask and loaf a little before I left the land of *dolce far niente*. To this end Florence is perfection. It is not a large town. From the Duomo near its center the most remote places of interest within the town are not more than a quarter of an hour's walk. As contrasted with Rome Florence has a friendly intimacy and tempts the visitor to stroll. Without knowing it you are at the Duomo and Giotto's Campanile, and a few steps farther at the Baptistry with its wonderful doors. You wander by Dante's House and soon come to the Bargello in which are Donatello's "David" and a remarkable collection of Michelangelo's sculptures. A little more and you are in the Piazza della Signoria in front of the Logia with Cellini's "Perseus" looking down on you, or you pass into the Uffizi Galleries which, united by a passageway over the Ponte Vecchio with the Pitti Palace, together house the most superb collections of Italian paintings the world over. That one collection of pictures should contain Botticelli's "Spring" and his "Birth of Venus," Michelangelo's "Holy Family," and Raphael's Madonnas, the Granduca, the della Sedia and others, means that you are in the very heart of Tuscan painting. To wander day after day through these magnificent galleries is to get some faint suggestion of that tremendous burst of Italian genius which produced them. What an age it must have been!

Life in Florence was easygoing. I found a very inviting restaurant near one of the large markets where I commonly took my midday meal. The menu was much the same as that at the Sereno in Naples, but in place of poor Nicolo there was a rather up-and-coming waiter, and everywhere the Tuscan tongue, the speech that Dante in his *Divine Comedy* had set for his whole race. In place of Posilipo Vecchio in quintos we had generous flasks of Chianti, sealed not with a cork but with a thin layer of olive oil across the neck. When the meal was over the waiter would lift the flask, estimate the amount of wine you had taken, and charge you accordingly. The wine was delicious and I have often wondered if an oil seal was not a better one for the bouquet of wine than a cork, the tannic acid of which must be no improvement. Still there is the resinated wine of Greece that most true Greeks crave! How much of wine is the cork? I must admit that the oil-sealed Chianti of Florence was to me the most fragrant and delicate ordinary table wine that I ever put to my lips.

Florence, like other Italian towns, has interesting and beautiful surroundings. Fiesoli, a comfortable walk of an hour and a half from Florence, commands a beautiful view of the larger city with its towers and the Duomo. A longer trip from Florence than Fiesoli is Pisa. I went one morning by train and spent the day there; part of the time in the Campo Santo and part about the Duomo. As I approached the Campo Santo which is filled, we are told, with ship loads of earth from the Holy Land, I was accosted by a ragged boy who shouted at me "Teamez, Teamez," and at the same time held up a much-worn copy of the London *Times*. It was over three weeks old and I declined it to look at still more ancient things. Such is relativity! Of the many antiquities in the Campo Santo, some of which are associated with Giovanni Pisano of pulpit fame, I was most interested in the "Triumph of Death," a painting attributed to Andrea Orcagna. As I looked at it I recalled a wedding-present made to my maternal grandmother, which also represented the world in process of being separated into the good and the bad. The latter, as they walked along, some with bottles in their hands, others with different instruments of depravity about them, were one by one falling off the cliff into the Eternal Abyss, while a very, very few others with saintly faces and averted eyes were tracing with difficulty the narrow but sure road to Eternal Bliss. The donor of this gift framed it himself for my grandmother. Our family tradition had it that he was an undertaker. Could he have been a rejected suitor or was the gift made in the spirit that prompted, I am sure, the work on the "Triumph of Death" in Pisa? This is the only echo that has ever come to me of what my grandmother's wedding must have been like. It was this part of my family who told me that going to Harvard was going to Perdition.

Pisa, however, was much more than the Campo Santo. It was the laboratory, natural and primitive in all respects, of Galileo. Here in the cathedral hung the lamp whose swinging gave to this great

scientist the idea of the pendulum, and outside still stands the campanile, the Leaning Tower of Pisa, from the top of which he studied
the laws of falling bodies. How strange the contrast between what
is left of the belief behind the "Triumph of Death" and of that
from Galileo's discoveries. The "Triumph" has come to be at best
an interesting piece of fictitious, poetic invention. Galileo's work
has been built into the solid foundations of our modern conception
of what the world about us is like, a contribution which day by
day grows more enduring as Science progresses.

My rest and delight in Florence and its surroundings restored my
balance, lost in a measure in Rome, and I was now ready to go on to
Venice. Here again the unique beauty of the place was balm to the
soul. As in Florence I did not press myself hard, but sauntered or
was carried about Venice in delightful indolence. My stopping place
was on the water, facing the mouth of the grand canal and very
close to San Marco. Much of the beauty of Venice is external. The
houses, the churches, and especially the palaces are incrusted with
the finest stone-work; most notable among these are the Doges'
Palace and the Church of St. Mark with its four golden horses. In
the open, unprotected except by the General's fierce frown, stands
the wonderful equestrian statue of Bartolommeo Colleoni by
Verrocchio. To stroll about in the neighborhood of these beautiful
objects is to enjoy them in surroundings of simple and perfect
harmony. Even the pigeons in the Piazza of St. Mark play their
appropriate parts. Indoors in Venice are hosts of paintings by members of the Venetian School, the Bellinis, Carpaccio, Tintoretto, and
Titian. Of these, the story of St. Ursula and her Virgins, as told by
Carpaccio in the series of paintings at the academy, appealed to me
most strongly. Perhaps this was due to the fact that at Harvard
Professor Moore helped me copy a copy made by him of St. Ursula
sleeping. But, after all, the impression that Venice makes is not so
much in its details, exquisite though they are, as in its totality, a
sense of all-pervading beauty. Some years after this, my first visit
to Venice, when my wife and I revisited this city of canals, Mrs.
Parker inquired for a certain gondolier who had been engaged to
come with his gondola to the Chicago World's Fair and had taken
her on several trips on the lagoon at the Fair. To our surprise he
was at that moment on the grand canal and came at once to us at a
call from the hotel. He gave us a wonderful ride, in course of which

we talked to him about his American experiences. He said he had never before been far from Venice till he went to Chicago. He frankly declared he had never known that there could be such ugly cities as Chicago and New York, and that after having seen them he longed for Venice. He added further that nothing could ever bring him to separate himself again from the beauty of his native town. And so it is. Venice is pervaded with beauty as few other places are. But my days in Italy were drawing to a close. Two issues were beginning to force themselves upon me: my time for travel was running out and my resources were getting low.

I still had several stops to make before I sailed for home. I must go to Paris and to England and, as it was now July and my return to America was set for August, these visits would of necessity be short ones. I left Venice by train and traveled through the Tyrol and over the Brenner Pass and thus to Innsbruck, whence after a short stop to see my old Berlin friend, Dr. Heider, I went on to Munich. Here I presented a card of introduction to Professor Richard Hertwig who, as soon as he had shaken hands with me, told me that I was engaged to come with him for supper at the Hofbrau. I then visited his laboratory where I met Dr. C. R. Eastman from Harvard who was studying there. In the evening Professor Hertwig and a group of younger zoologists took me to the Hofbrau where I enjoyed warm, Bavarian hospitality. On that day and the next I visited the Pinakothek collections old and new and the Glyptothek, and on the day following I took train for Paris. We were told that we were to have two hours at the French frontier for the examination of baggage and for a table d'hôte. As we moved onward I noticed that the German train was steadily losing time and I asked the conductor what would happen to passengers who were going through to Paris and who had ordered in advance a midday meal at the frontier station. He assured me that we would be cared for and we were. On the arrival of the German train we were immediately ushered into the dining room, seated at table, and told the French train left in seven minutes. The table d'hôte was there before us and it is remarkable how much food can be consumed in seven minutes. As an American I thought we were a nation of rapid movers, but I am forced to admit that under stress of circumstances European travelers can exceed us. Soup was drunk from a cup; the cutlet and vegetable were dispatched so quickly that I took a second helping; salad was omitted; dessert, a tart, I put in a napkin and carried onto the train that I might take time enough at the station to enjoy a demitasse; and all in about the time it has taken me to write this sentence. Now we were on our way to Paris.

I arrived in the French capital late in the evening. Here I was met by a friend who knew of my coming. He told me that the French zoologists whom I would wish to see were all out of town. This I had feared might be the case. I made up my mind, however, to see the shell if I could not have the kernel, and the next morning I began doing the sights of Paris in a mild way.

For a biologist the Jardin des Plantes is an institution of first importance, for this was the scene of one of the world's great biological revolutions. Originally intended for a collection of medicinal plants the Jardin was soon brought to embrace plants of all kinds as well as animals and minerals and thus became a great natural history center. Bounded by the Rue Buffon, Rue Geoffroy St. Hilaire, and Rue Cuvier its biological, and particularly its zoological, tendencies were manifest. Its transformation from an herb garden to a center of natural history was accomplished by Buffon who in 1739 became its director. In Buffon's day the naturalist who dealt with plants and animals was chiefly concerned in describing them so that they could be identified. Buffon, however, had wider views on this subject, and pointed out the importance of comparing as well as describing different kinds of living things. The comparative method thus introduced became in the hands of those who worked in the Jardin an all-pervading principle. It was seized upon by two of the younger men, Geoffroy St. Hilaire and particularly Cuvier, both of whom stressed it in their life's work. Cuvier, who was profoundly interested in the fossils of the Paris basin, showed that, in conformity with this principle, extinct animals were like living ones in that their skeletons were made of corresponding bones. This discovery enabled Cuvier to predict, from what were often very scanty fossil remains, the general features of the rest of a fossil skeleton, a prediction which, with the discovery of a more nearly complete specimen, was often fully verified. In this way Cuvier demonstrated the intimate relation between fossil and recent animals, and the importance of using living animals as a means of understanding fossils. Cuvier may thus be said to have been the founder of two important movements in the biological field; comparative anatomy, whereby different animals were shown to have much in common in their plans of structure, and modern paleontology, or the interpretation of fossils by a comparison with living forms. Although the successful growth of this revolutionary movement must be attributed chiefly to Cuvier, its initiation is to be found in the early speculations of Buffon and its promotion depended upon a number of other investigators such as Geoffroy St. Hilaire. All these scholars were associated with the Jardin des Plantes and this institution may thus be looked upon as the cradle of the comparative method. From the Jardin as a center this doctrine was disseminated abroad, especially in England, by Owen, and in America, by Louis Agassiz. The latter, a Swiss naturalist, in founding his museum at Harvard after his transfer to America designated that institution as the Museum of Comparative Zoölogy. In course of time schools of comparative anatomy flourished in Germany under Gegenbaur and Wiedersheim. Thus, all students of the biological sciences, and particularly those of zoology, must look upon the Jardin des Plantes as the center from which has come a world-wide movement in their several fields; a movement with the underlying conception of an all-pervading unity in organic nature.

The full meaning of this unifying principle was not grasped by most of the early members of this school. To a few, as for instance to Geoffroy St. Hilaire, it meant family connections among relatively diverse organisms, plants and animals, with perhaps community of descent of all from a common stock. On this point Geoffroy St. Hilaire disagreed absolutely with the others and especially with Cuvier, as such a view was repugnant to Cuvier and most of his immediate followers. In fact, between Geoffroy and Cuvier the matter grew to be one of personal animosity. But the evolutionary tendencies of Geoffroy, as they would be called today, were by no means so radical as were those of another investigator in the Jardin, namely, Lamarck. This worker, in his early years a student of plants and in his later life a student of animals, was a reserved and reticent personality whose views received scant attention from his colleagues at the Jardin. As a speculative writer, Lamarck was less interested in the comparison of living things than he was in the unity of organic plan thus discovered. That unity he believed to be the result of a community of descent; in other words he was a convinced evolutionist. In this respect he was far in advance of most of his associates, but his speculations on this theme were so unusual, and at times so bizarre, that the small but significant germ of truth contained in them was lost in the large body of useless disputation.

The recognition of this germ of truth was slow in coming and arrived only long after Lamarck's death. It is significant that the streets which surround the Jardin bear the names of Lamarck's colleagues, but that there is no thoroughfare honored by his cognomen. The memorial to Lamarck is to be seen in his statue at the entrance to the Jardin, a statue which was not erected until 1909, the centennial anniversary of the publication of his chief evolutionary volume, *La Philosophie Zoologique*. The erection of this memorial was accomplished only after the importance of Lamarck as a speculative biologist had been recognized. Thus the Jardin is not only a center whence emanated the doctrine of comparison for organisms, but it is one of the earliest institutions concerned with the promulgation of the theory of organic evolution. For these reasons it must always remain a place of profound historical interest to the biologist.

A second place that I felt I must visit during my very short stay in Paris was Auteuil, a suburb near the southeast corner of the Bois de Boulogne. The cemetery of Auteuil contains the grave of Benjamin Thompson, Count Rumford, and his last residence is marked on the Rue d'Auteuil. As a student at Harvard I had on several occasions walked to North Woburn, some twelve miles from Cambridge, where stands the colonial farmhouse in which Benjamin Thompson, a country lad, was born in 1753. I have also frequented the Old Oyster House on Union Street, Boston, which in provincial days was Hopestill Capen's emporium for the sale of laces and silks to the well-to-do ladies of the town and in which Benjamin Thompson was for a time an apprentice. In my mind's eye I can follow him to Concord, then to Rumford, New Hampshire, where he married a lady who brought him wealth, and then after her death to England where he found service in the colonial department of the British government. In 1779 he was elected to the Royal Society of London, and later he was active in founding the Royal Institute. He then transferred to the Electorate of Bavaria where he reorganized government and army. In the Bavarian arsenal he became interested in the heat generated in boring cannon and published an account of the process with a determination of the mechanical equivalent of heat. This determination was remarkable, considering the means at his disposal, and gave him a high place among the distinguished men of science of his day. In Bavaria he was honored by being made a Count of the Holy Roman Empire, and when he was asked for a special designation he declared for Count Rumford, after the town of his early married life. He returned to England in 1798 and then four years later took up residence in Paris. Here he married the widow of the celebrated French chemist Lavoisier who had been guillotined during the early days of the French Revolution. He and his new wife lived in her villa at Auteuil till his death in 1814. His will contained bequests to the Royal Society in London, to the American Academy of Arts and Sciences in Boston, and to Harvard College. With the funds thus received all these institutions established foundations for the advancement of the physical sciences and designated them as Rumford Funds. The scientifically adventurous life of this Yankee farmboy had always interested me, and as I knew his birthplace well I resolved that should I ever have the good fortune to visit Paris I would seek out his last resting place. This now I had done.

I could not remain long in Paris, but I visited, of course, Notre Dame, the Louvre and other places of general interest and then betook myself to Havre for a passage across the channel to Southampton. I had been on the continent all of two years. How strange it would be to come to a land where my native tongue would be spoken and where I could converse without let or hindrance! What was my surprise when I discovered that I could scarcely make out what was said to me by the people on the docks of Southampton. They might well have been entire strangers to me speaking in a foreign tongue. I took train at once for London, and here to my relief I found that the spoken language of the day was understandable English.

London proved to be like Paris. The zoologists whom I wished to see were, for the most part, out of town. While I was wandering through the zoological collections of the British Museum I met by accident Dr. S. J. Hickson of the zoological department of Manchester University. I had previously made his acquaintance in

Boston when, some years before, he had been traveling in the United States. Hickson kindly invited me to the Savile Club in London for luncheon, and there I had the additional pleasure of meeting Professor E. Ray Lancaster, head of the zoological department at Oxford. Professor Lancaster regretted that the Oxford laboratories were closed and told me that it would be useless for me to make a trip there. I did, however, go to Oxford for a day. I declined Baedeker's suggestion that if pressed for time in visiting the English universities Oxford will be found sufficient, and I spent a day at Cambridge. Here, out of respect to John Harvard, I visited Emmanuel College. In the Cambridge zoological laboratory I found one lone zoologist, Dr. Sidney F. Harmer, who very kindly entertained me at luncheon and took me for a beautiful walk along the Cam. But I was speeding homeward and after this very short visit to Cambridge I returned directly to London. Here I spent two or three days sight-seeing and then recrossed the channel to make my way to Rotterdam and the steamer for America.

In Rotterdam money for my homeward passage was to have been waiting for me, but it had failed to arrive. I counted my pennies and found that I had just enough for a second-class ticket on the next Dutch liner sailing in a day or two for New York. This, by a strange coincidence, was the *Werkendam*, the same boat on which I had crossed two years before on my outward passage. Meanwhile I telegraphed an old friend then in France for a small loan of money to enable me to change from second to first-class on the boat about to sail. By good fortune my friend was within reach, could accommodate me, and just before the *Werkendam* sailed I was able to transfer to first-class. The passage to New York was quiet, uneventful, and with a very small passenger list, for at that time of year, July, there were very few passengers traveling westward. Some eight or ten of us sat at the captain's table and between meals beguiled ourselves by reading, telling experiences, and watching the sea till the shores of America appeared on the horizon.

XV

Settling in the New World

CAMBRIDGE

NICEST PLACE THAT EVER WAS SEEN,—
COLLEGES RED AND COMMON GREEN,
SIDEWALKS BROWNISH WITH TREES BETWEEN.
SWEETEST SPOT BENEATH THE SKIES
WHEN THE CANKER-WORMS DON'T RISE,—
WHEN THE DUST, THAT SOMETIMES FLIES
INTO YOUR MOUTH AND EARS AND EYES,
IN A QUIET SLUMBER LIES.

O. W. Holmes

THUS far nothing has been said about the most important and all-significant event of this period in my life, the attempt to find Mrs. G. H. Parker. I felt sure that she was somewhere in the world, if I could only come up with her. There had been the usual number of premonitory ripples on the lake of my affections, but not until June 1888 did the actual tempest of waves break. It occurred on Harvard Class Day of that year, and partly through the intervention of two of my college friends. At the opening of the academic year in September 1887 I was the only graduate student in the Harvard zoological laboratory, but I was soon joined by two others, Herbert H. Field and Charles B. Davenport, both of whom came from Brooklyn, New York. These two students were entered in Harvard as undergraduates, to be transferred after they had established their standing to the then growing graduate department. Field took his Harvard bachelor's degree at commencement in June 1888 and consequently celebrated the event on Class Day of that year. This was the period in Harvard's history of glorious Class Day festivities. The morning of this joyous day was given over to exercises open only to the members of the graduating class who, dressed in the remarkable garb of tailed coats and high hats, marched and remarched about the college buildings. In the early afternoon all this was changed and the class members, now attired in their roughest clothes, in the presence of a very select group of guests back of Harvard Hall danced around the Class Day Tree. Here they sang college songs and cheered Harvard, the President, the favorite professors, and most of all the ladies. High on the trunk of the Class Day Tree, a venerable elm, was a broad band of innumerable small bouquets. At a signal given from the class marshal, by throwing his high hat into the air, the members of the class rushed en masse to the tree, each one intent on gaining a bouquet for some fair one among the many onlookers. The last bouquet, highest of all on the tree and in consequence most difficult to carry off, called for concerted action with evidence of popularity for certain competing members in the class. The scrimmage lasted a full quarter of an hour, after which the seniors, in tatters, rushed off to bathe and change for the less strenuous doings of the afternoon. These consisted of the "Spreads" where each senior, now again attired in tail coat and high hat, entertained his invited guests with ample refreshments and other social amenities. The "Spreads" were held for the most part in college rooms on the Yard and gradually merged into the general evening performances with an illumination of the Yard, music, dancing, singing by the glee club, and a grand promenade under thousands of Chinese lanterns.

Field invited Davenport and me to his "Spread," held in rooms in Stoughton Hall. Here we met a delightful company, including Field's family and a number of his relatives and friends. As the "Spread" was drawing to a close Davenport and I stepped out of Stoughton Hall and were standing in the Yard near the college pump when Field's father approached and introduced us to five of the young women of his party, and with a sense a evident relief suggested that we escort them about the Yard. The general illumination had already begun and we took the girls to the singing by the glee club in front of Sever Hall, to the band concerts in different parts of the Yard, and to the promenade after which we saw them to the various meeting places appointed by their elders. One of the party, Miss Louise Stabler, was to be brought to her aunt, Mrs. Field, at a house on Appian Way. I therefore proposed to conduct her there, and together she and I walked from the College Yard to her destination, a distance of a quarter of a mile or so. Out

of the heat of the Yard we found the evening one of beautiful, cool
moonlight. Although in the Yard I had enjoyed the company of the
party in our care I do not recall that I was impressed by one girl
more than by another. A short time later, however, after I had
walked with Miss Stabler to her Appian Way address and had said
adieu to her I had a very different opinion. I was convinced that I
had at last found the future Mrs. Parker, if my wishes could prevail. The next day several of us took the same party of girls to a
college baseball game on Holmes' Field. Here again I saw Miss
Stabler and my private opinion of the night before was confirmed.
Who could have described such happening at Harvard in better
words than Dr. Holmes when he wrote:

> *Pleasant place for boys to play;—*
> *Better keep your girls away;*
> *Hearts get rolled as pebbles do*
> *Which countless fingering waves pursue.*

And so it proved for me.

It is quite impossible in happenings of this kind to fathom their
real depth. What is there in a succession of daily events that suddenly brings a person to a point-blank decision which he knows,
even after many years, could not have been better settled? Our
elders tell us that such steps should be taken only after mature
deliberation, but in this instance there was no deliberation at all
and I find it difficult to ascribe my sudden resolve to anything in
particular. I do recall a feature about Miss Stabler that attracted
my attention: of the five girls whom we escorted about the Yard,
she was the most simply dressed. Nor was her attire new nor in the
latest mode. Yet she entered into the enjoyment of the occasion as
freely as any of us and without the least possible concern about her
apparel. I seemed to gain the impression that she was a girl of
unusual good sense who held the material values in life where they
belong. Perhaps I gathered subconsciously that considering what
my way of living was likely to be she would prove in these respects
a fitting companion. But this is mostly ratiocination, and even if
these ideas did go through my head they had, I am sure, a very
small part in shaping my final determination. This turned on the
intuition that at last the woman of my choice had appeared, and
there was an end of it. How such emotional resolves arise is hard

to say. Only those who have experienced them know their impelling force. I, at least, felt the full clarity of a new awakening. What was I to do? I resolved to let my feelings mature.

During the next three years or so, as I traveled back and forth between Philadelphia and Cambridge, I occasionally met Miss Stabler who lived on Brooklyn Heights, not far from her aunt and uncle the Fields. Acquaintance gradually ripened into friendship. Herbert Field, during the latter part of his university life at Harvard, lived with my family in Cambridge, and thus the Fields and their connections grew in intimacy with my people. I became a calling acquaintance at the Fields and the Stablers. For two or three days before I sailed for Europe in 1891 I was a guest at the Fields' summer residence at Great Neck, Long Island. At that time Miss Stabler was also staying with her aunt at Great Neck. On the evening of July 2, my last day before sailing, I spoke to Miss Stabler about my growing attachment for her and begged her to consider marriage with me, if she could think well of it, after my return from Europe. She declined my proposal, but not in a way that made me regard her reply as final and I asked her to hold my request as binding so far as I was concerned and to let the matter rest till she could come to her own decision. This interview was close to the Field garden where we together earlier in the day had picked bunches of sweet peas for the adornment of the house, blossoms which in subsequent years became our family flower. I did not sleep much during the night of July 2, nor had I any appetite for breakfast on the following morning. I then bade the Fields and their friends adieus and later in the day I boarded the *Werkendam* for Holland, to find myself well out on the Atlantic on July 4, 1891, as already related.

The winter following, in Leipzig, was in some ways lonely, for I had been requested not to write to Miss Stabler. In the spring of the next year I learned that she was to accompany her aunt and uncle for a summer trip to Europe and that Dr. H. H. Field was to meet the party in Germany and travel with them. I found that I would not be *de trop* and hence I arranged to make the Rhein tour with the party on July 22. On the morning of that day we took the Rhein boat at Mainz and reached Cologne before evening, after a day of wonderful weather and river scenery. In the evening Miss Stabler and I took a walk to the cathedral which was very close to the hotel at which we were stopping. We went round and round this structure discussing the all-absorbing question, and when we left it for the hotel I was, if not wholly happy, at least very contented. The situation was well described by Mr. Field, Miss Stabler's uncle, who remarked that "If those two young people are not already engaged they ought to be," and so I thought. Miss Stabler, however, preferred not to have it "come out," for she was still in college and she asked me to hold all in abeyance till my return from Europe the year following. The next day the Fields and Miss Stabler continued their journey and I returned by train to Berlin. Here Dr. Korschelt had noticed my absence from the laboratory and looked at me inquiringly on my return. I replied in simple but truthful polyglot, "Ich bin noch nicht engaged aber ich bin verlobt." All of which meant that my doings were not to be reported to America, but might be mentioned in Germany. He was interested to learn that the young lady of my choice was a cousin of Dr. H. H. Field with whom he had already become acquainted. Thus, so far as Miss Stabler and I were concerned, a *sub rosa* arrangement was consummated which was reasonably satisfactory to both of us. As to the trip down the river, one conspicuous deficiency must be mentioned. When, on July 22, Miss Stabler arrived in Cologne after having made the Rhein tour, she seemed to have not the least remembrance of the beautiful scenery which makes up the shores of that beautiful river. I believe that she did recollect that Ehrenbreitstein was on the east bank of the Rhein. During the trip her mind was probably otherwise occupied. To make up for this blank in her tour I felt called upon to send her a set of photographs of the Rhein between Mainz and Cologne in the hope that if called upon to speak of the Rhein in America she would be able to talk intelligently about this historic stream. After leaving Germany, our American visitors completed their summer's outing by continuing their trip through the low countries, France, and Great Britain after which they took boat for New York. This was the summer of 1892 when the great outbreak of Asiatic cholera took place in Hamburg. One of the German liners from that port had serious trouble at its New York terminal, but I was greatly relieved to learn that the vessel on which the Fields and Miss Stabler traveled discharged its passengers at the American destination without difficulties. Late that summer after I had finished my work at the

University of Berlin I went to St. Andreasberg in the Harz for a little respite before proceeding to Freiburg im Breisgau for the winter semester. Toward the end of my sojourn in Berlin much concern was expressed about a possible outbreak of cholera in that city and, consequently, I did not overstay my time, but I found this another reason for a visit to the Harz where cholera had never been known to come. I left my salubrious mountain resort early in September with a third-class ticket for Freiburg im Breisgau. At Fulda our train was stopped and two coaches were taken off. I was told that they both had proved to have cholera cases among their occupants. Passengers were redistributed and isolated. As I came from the Harz and was in no way complicated by the cholera situation I found myself put alone in a second-class compartment. Farther up the line toward Frankfurt the train was again stopped, a cholera-suspect removed, and certain passengers redistributed. This time I found myself again alone, and now in a first-class compartment. I am frank to state that the railroad management was most considerate of us in all these readjustments. At Frankfurt we were discharged from the train within a cordon of local police who were supposed to examine us and pass on us as to health, but we all took to our heels and no one was the wiser or, so far as I ever learned, the sicker. Beyond Frankfurt the phantom of cholera ceased to follow me. From this town I made my way with much deliberation up the Rhein Valley via Heidelberg, Speyer, Strasburg, and Colmar to Freiburg im Breisgau. Here, as already mentioned, I spent the winter semester and then went to Italy for the spring. I left Naples in June and after rather rapid traveling I reached New York August 4, 1893, having been abroad exactly two years and a month.

I went at once to the Stabler's in Brooklyn where my first act after meeting my fiancée was to borrow five dollars from her to repay a sum which had been loaned me by a Dutch acquaintance on the *Werkendam* so that I might leave the vessel free of small debts. The immediateness with which Miss Stabler responded to this request seemed to me to augur well, for, as she once told me in connection with other matters, our actual acquaintance was very limited. The total length of time that we had spent together from our first meeting at Class Day, 1888, till my return from Europe in 1893, when she allowed me to say that we were engaged, was a period to be counted not so much in days as in hours, a statement literally true.

And now, as my fiancée said, I was to be shown off to her family. To this I had no objection so long as we performed the rites together. In a way it was a matriarchal ceremony, for the senior member of the family was my fiancée's great-aunt Hannah Field, who, an elderly Quaker woman of some ninety years, was one in whom I found a great charm and for whom I came to entertain a strong affection. She recalled to me both my paternal grandmother and Lucretia Mott, two women who had meant so much to me in my youth. Aunt Hannah was the last of her generation and lived in the old Field homestead, Pine Cottage, very close to the New York-Connecticut state line and a few miles north of Port Chester. Here my fiancée had passed many of her summer vacations and had learned most of what she knew of farm life, including driving and riding horses and even driving oxen. To Pine Cottage we went not only then, but many times thereafter. Of course we also saw Mr. and Mrs. Field, and I was greatly amused at Mrs. Field's remark that when she and her husband took Miss Stabler under their care for her European trip Mrs. Field told Miss Stabler's mother that she, Mrs. Field, would be responsible in all respects for Miss Stabler except in so far as Howard Parker was concerned. Evidently our elders or at least their womenfolk had kept their eyes open.

From Brooklyn and my fiancée's family I continued my homeward trip to Cambridge where I found my mother and my two sisters much as I had left them. I had been reappointed as instructor in zoology at Harvard and I quickly slipped into the traces. The past year had been a bad one for the university. Harvard had concluded 1892–93 with a deficit of some six thousand dollars. President Eliot was much concerned, for with him any deficit was a serious matter. Some very judicious academic pruning was undertaken, even to the enforced withdrawal of certain professors. The President looked worried. Mrs. Eliot remarked: "Poor Mr. Eliot does nothing but go about turning out gas-lights to save expense." True, it was a critical year. I fortunately held my place, and the university of course survived, in fact, during the following year Harvard's income began to catch up. It was not a period, however, in which expansion could be indulged in. We worked hard at the treadmill.

My own affairs, however, were such that it seemed to Miss Stabler and me that we might contemplate matrimony. She had graduated in the first class from Barnard College in June 1893. During the following winter she took graduate work at Barnard, did some tutoring, and attended evening classes in household affairs at Pratt Institute in Brooklyn. Taking all in all we seemed to be prepared for marriage, and on the thirty-fifth anniversary of Mrs. Stabler's wedding day, June 15, 1894, we became man and wife.

Ours was a Quaker wedding, that is, it was under the Religious Society of Friends. Our request so to marry, much in advance of the ceremony, was handed to the New York Friends' Meeting for consideration. Miss Stabler was a member of that Meeting and was well known there. I was not a member of any Friends' group, but was expected to be present at a given session of the New York Meeting. I went as appointed, sat quietly through the period, and then having heard our request read and recorded was about to go when an elderly Friend turned to me and asked me as a stranger what brought me hither. I told him I was taking steps to get a wife. Thereupon he said, "Oh! Thee is Howard Parker and thee wishes to marry Louise Stabler." To which I assented and he, apparently satisfied, walked away. We were to have a home wedding at the house of Mrs. Stabler on Brooklyn Heights, where in fact Miss Stabler had been born. Here on the appointed afternoon our two families and their friends assembled, a party of perhaps some fifty persons. When all had gathered, Miss Stabler and I entered the room and after a short period of quiet we, in our own words, pledged ourselves to be husband and wife. We then signed the wedding certificate which, after it had been read aloud by one of the Friends, was also signed by the guests present. Among those at the wedding, certain ones had been designated by the New York Meeting as a committee to see that the ceremony was performed properly, and to report to the Meeting for record. All was duly accomplished.

My only surviving near-relative in Philadelphia, a maiden aunt, was unable to attend our wedding. She was a very strict member of the Methodist Church, and when the details of our ceremony were given to her she was almost scandalized to learn that there had been no minister present. To her this seemed an omission which meant that we were really not wholly married and I never was able to convince her that we were as completely man and wife as any

couple who took the step before a "hireling minister," as Friends
would say.

Our situation was, in a measure, quite the reverse of the experience of a foreign cousin and his fiancée. They had shortly before
come to this country and had become married without knowing it.
Thus: they had made their plans for matrimony only to discover
from the city clerk to whom they had applied for a marriage license
that the date which they had decided upon was so near at hand that
an ordinary license would not be sufficient. They were advised by
the clerk to take their license to a county judge, state their case,
and if the judge saw fit, obtain from him a waiver so that the time
limit in their license could be dispensed with. This they did and
then asked what was the next step. They were told to go back to
the city clerk and present their papers. They at once followed this
advice. The clerk then asked them about their intentions and filled
out certain papers which they willingly signed and in full confidence that they were now prepared for marriage they separated;
she to go to her own residence and he to go home for further
preparations for the marriage set for a few days later. This ceremony they believed was to be completed by a minister of the
church. When, however, the future bridegroom described to us
the details of what had transpired during his last visit to the city
clerk it was clear that without understanding what they were doing
they had taken the final step and were really already married. This
discovery called for immediate action. Their proposed wedding day
was made into a reception day and the wrongly dated announce-
ments of their wedding were destroyed and a new set correctly
dated were quickly prepared. Which is worse, to have your relatives
tell you that you are married when you did not suppose you were
or to say to you that you are not married when you believe the step
to have been taken? This seems like a serious question, but I doubt
if young people in the matrimonial state of mind take such matters to heart.

But to continue with my own marriage! My fiancée and I had
unconventionally wished to walk after our ceremony, the short
distance from her home to the annex ferryboat in Brooklyn by
which we could be carried to the evening boat of the Fall River
Line. But the family ruled against this and a carriage had been
ordered. By a strange coincidence the carriage failed to appear at

the house on time and thus, as a matter of fact, we had our own way. We probably met the vehicle as we walked down the street, bags in hand, but it was too late. We were going to Nantucket for our honeymoon. From Fall River the next day we crossed by train to New Bedford where we took the Nantucket boat. At Nantucket no one was to discover that we were newly wed. Our clothes were old, our traveling bags were old, and our trunk was old. Even we ourselves were not especially young. We stopped at a very agreeable and well-established boardinghouse and we carried out our deception fairly well, till at a meal soon after we arrived I offered Mrs. Parker some fish, to which she replied "I never eat fish." The game was up! Those at the table had the laugh on us and we admitted the charge. Marriage is a sure step to the discovery of many strange things. My wife said that one of her greatest surprises was to find that when I prepared for bed I did not take off my beard. Nantucket was an ideal place for a honeymoon, but all good things have an end, and after some weeks there we returned to Brooklyn, packed our belongings, and made our way to Cambridge.

In the university town we stayed with my mother and sisters while we sought a habitation of our own. This we soon found in a house near the Harvard botanical garden, in an agreeably open part of Cambridge. Our maid of all work was paid two dollars and a half a week! Incredible, yet true!! Our house was surrounded by shade trees and fruit trees. Our landlord, Mr. Dudley, and his family lived next to us and were more than kind in helping us start married life. On Mr. Dudley's death, which occurred not long after our arrival, we were under the care of Mrs. Dudley as our landlady. Some years later she found reason to increase the rent on several pieces of property owned by her and near at hand. We had no lease for the house we were occupying and I looked for a like increase in our rent. Nothing of the kind, however, happened and on inquiry Mrs. Dudley told us that we were to remain in the house we occupied at the original rent and for as long as we wished, for, said she: "Did not Mr. Parker hold a lighted lamp over my only son when the afternoon light failed, and our family physician was operating on him for appendicitis?" Are we to believe that friendliness is better than a bond? So it seemed and so it has proved.

As my wife and I settled into Cambridge life two significant events occurred, one a joy, the other a great sadness. Our Philadelphia friend, Miss Adeline Tryon, invited my wife and me to be her companions for the summer of 1896 in a trip to Europe, the culmination of which was to be a week at Bayreuth where we were to attend a full performance of Wagner's *Ring of the Niebelungs.* This was indeed a rare and wonderful experience. But it was coupled with a very sad event, for on our way back to America we were notified of the unexpected death of my younger sister, who, though ailing when we left, was not supposed to be seriously ill. It was a shock from which those of us who knew her well never recovered. Life is indeed a checkered pattern of the gay and the sad.

XVI

Seaside Laboratories

IN THE LAP OF SHELTERING SEAS
RESTS THE ISLE OF PENIKESE;
BUT THE LORD OF THE DOMAIN
COMES NOT TO HIS OWN AGAIN.

. . . .

OTHER LIPS WITHIN ITS BOUND
SHALL THE LAWS OF LIFE EXPOUND;
OTHER EYES FROM ROCK AND SHELL
READ THE WORLD'S OLD RIDDLES WELL.

J. G. Whittier

THE Anderson School of Natural History, a seaside laboratory founded and conducted by Louis Agassiz on the island of Penikese in the summer of 1873, and carried on after his death for a second summer by a number of his more advanced students, called out repercussions that were not anticipated at the time. Soon after the Penikese experiment, the Naples station was started on the Italian Mediterranean, and after that the English Plymouth, followed then by a goodly number of international marine laboratories the world over. Not that Penikese first gave to biologists the idea of a marine laboratory. Rather was it that this idea was in the air and that Penikese was among the first realizations of it in America. What Penikese did directly, however, was to act as an instigator of the group of seaside laboratories situated at Woods Hole, Massachusetts, the laboratory of the United States Fisheries Bureau, the Marine Biological Laboratory, and the Woods Hole Oceanographic Institute. The earliest of these to settle at Woods Hole was the laboratory of the Fisheries Bureau, or as it was then called the laboratory of the United States Fish Commission. This institution was located at Woods Hole for two reasons: accessibility to train and boat service, and the richness of the marine life there. The town of

Woods Hole is on the mainland and is therefore easy to reach at all seasons of the year and in all kinds of weather, conditions very unlike these of the Island of Penikese. Further, the fauna and flora of Woods Hole and the neighboring waters are quite as rich as are those of Penikese, a location which had been chosen for the unusual variety of organisms representative of both northern and southern waters. If Penikese pointed out the general region for a satisfactory seaside laboratory, Woods Hole established the final spot.

Why is it that biologists the world over tend to seek the seashore? The answer is simple. The sea is the home of living things. Here life originated and from this source it has spread over the rest of the globe. Evidence for this is seen in so simple a matter as the present distribution of animals. Zoologists nowadays divide all animals into some fifteen major groups, such as the backbone creatures, the mollusks, the arthropods, including the insects and the crabs, the various groups of worms, the corals and jellyfishes, sponges, and the microscopic one-cell animals. Of these fifteen groups, only six are represented on the land, eleven are met with in fresh water, but all fifteen are to be found in the sea. Hence it is fair to conclude that not only animal life but the main groups of animals originated in the sea, that members from eleven of these groups then made their way into fresh water, and that of these fresh water creatures representatives of six groups migrated onto the land. When a biologist goes to the sea he is entering the home of animal life where all the chief groups of the animal kingdom are still present. The sea contains creatures that range in size from the microscopic luminous one-cell forms that in countless billions light up tropical waters, to the largest single animal now living, the sulphur-bottom whale which may measure somewhat over ninety feet in length. The sea is the place par excellence for the study of animal life in its full range. Hence the genesis of the marine laboratories!

To Woods Hole, for years past, American and foreign biologists, young and old, have flocked in great numbers. My first visit there, a very short one, was in the summer of 1888. The laboratory of the Fish Commission was then in full operation, and here I worked for a brief period. This year, 1888, was the first year of the Marine Biological Laboratory. The Oceanographic Institute did not begin operations till much later, in 1931. After my brief visit to the laboratory of the United State Fish Commission, I resolved, if possible, to spend a summer there, and I was fortunate enough to arrange for this the next year, 1889. In the laboratory I found a group of perhaps a dozen or more investigators, some young, some old, studying the marine creatures of the New England seaside. At that time my interests were in the structure and growth of the compound eyes of the lobster and other crustaceans. As the Fish Commission was then much concerned with the propagation of the lobster in the waters about Woods Hole, the laboratory was in consequence a very favorable place for my work and I found more than enough material to keep me busy for the whole season. The laboratory building was open day and night and there was a good fleet of collecting craft from a large steamboat, the *Fish Hawk,* to rowboats of all kinds so that facilities for outside work were quite ample.

The helpers about the laboratory were seafaring men whose youth had been passed on the open sea, but who in their later years had sought work on shore. Joe Gardner was a ship carpenter of excellent ability in making floats, cages, and other like equipment for work in the harbor. He had done much fishing in local waters, particularly for swordfish. On one occasion he and others were out well off No Mans Land when they sighted on a very smooth sea a swordfish basking in the sunlight. There was very little wind, but with patience they brought their small sloop up to within striking distance and were lucky enough to harpoon the fish. The swordfish made off with line and keg, and Joe, resolving not to lose the prize, took to a skiff and rowed after them. At some distance from the sloop Joe came up with the keg and took it into the skiff, whereupon the fish started to tow both skiff and Joe at a fair rate till they were well away from sloop. Those on the sloop attempted to follow, but the wind was very light and they made little headway. After a while they saw Joe rise in the skiff, take off his coat, which he then seemed to put in the bow of his boat, and then began waving his arms. Those on the sloop did their best to come up with him, but the breeze was so light and the fish towed Joe about so irregularly that it was an hour or more before they came abreast of him. They then found that the swordfish had, earlier in the game, charged the skiff, driven its sword through the bow below the water-line and in its endeavor to free itself had broken off the end of its sword in the boat. Although it was thus free of the skiff it was

still held by the harpoon and line. The hole in the skiff was large
and Joe had taken off his coat and wedged it into the aperture to
keep from foundering. Eventually he and the swordfish were
brought aboard the sloop and the adventure ended. For some time
the Fisheries laboratory had the pierced woodwork from the skiff
and two pieces of the broken sword as evidence of Joe's adventure.
Whenever Joe related his experience he always emphasized the fact
that the swordfish charged the skiff from below and that the sword
came up through the bottom of the bow and between his legs for
he was sitting in the bow. And in conclusion he would say and if
you don't believe it there is the hole still, pointing to the space
between his two legs.

The fish-culturist at the Fisheries was Mr. Perdum, a very large,
stout, red-faced man. He was more of a shore man than the others
about the station, but he was nevertheless an excellent fisherman.
He always played a conspicuous part in the affairs of the village.
Woods Hole was inclined to be somewhat sleepy; certainly it did
not wake up to the fact, till several years after 1902, that that year
was the tercentenary of its discovery by the English navigator,
Bartholomew Gosnold. In 1602, Gosnold is said to have landed on
Cape Cod, which he named, on Martha's Vineyard which he also
named, and on Cuttyhunk—called by him Elizabeth Island in
honor of the Virgin Queen of his native land, a name now used for
the whole chain of islands from Nonamesset to Cuttyhunk. Not
to be outdone by their oversight, however, the Woods Holeians
decided to celebrate their tercentenary, even if a few years late,
and Mr. Perdum was elected to impersonate Bartholomew Gosnold.
A more appropriate individual could not have been found among
the local talent. Mr. Perdum, dressed in the habiliments of three
centuries earlier, was rowed to shore in an old craft properly decorated, a plank was put out on which he was to walk to the
beach to greet a second body of villagers dressed as Indians. Just as
Mr. Perdum stepped onto the plank a volley was fired unexpectedly
from the stern of his craft, the repercussion of which was such that
instead of landing on the beach Mr. Perdum fell into the sea. He
waded out of Great Harbor and he completed his part of the performance without cracking a smile. I wondered at the time if
Gosnold may not have avenged this tardiness of Woods Hole by
this untoward mishap.

A third member of the Fisheries staff known to us all was Vinal N. Edwards, the veteran collector for the station. He was an upright man if there ever was one, of unimpeachable character, and yet a real human being. He had charge of the *Blue Wing*, a small steamboat which served to bring from the outside waters material needed by the investigators at the laboratory. Vinal was a man of ready wit. On a trip to Vineyard Haven we once passed several vessels of the United States Navy with flags up and salutes firing, evidently participating in some naval function. In my innocence I asked Vinal how many guns for an admiral, to which he replied with extreme acidity "One, if you can hit him!" Vinal had no use for the Navy, for he believed all its personnel to be hard-drinkers. A seaman from the *Fish Hawk* failed to appear one night. Early the next morning Vinal was out in a skiff with a hook and line and soon showed the captain of the boat a drowned sailor with a nearly empty flask in his pocket. When Bon Ami first came on the market Vinal saw crates of it so marked on the railroad pier and asked us if we knew whether this new drink was intoxicating. As townmarshal, Vinal never took a chance.

I always enjoyed taking trips with him and he was always very free in granting me permission. I once started out with him for Cotamy Inlet on Martha's Vineyard, with the understanding that I should be dropped off the *Blue Wing* at Edgartown and picked up at the same place three or four hours later. I wished to go to Captain Cottle's general store in town to get one or more whale teeth ornamented with scrimshaw. Captain Cottle assured me that all such teeth that may have been in Edgartown had been sold years before and that there were none now to be found. Then, after a moment's thought, he suggested that I go to a cottage a mile or so off on Water Street where a woman was living whose husband was with the whaling fleet in the north, and who might have teeth of the kind I sought. I found the cottage but no tooth. When the woman learned that I was interested in such things she showed me a beautiful polar bear skin which she said her husband wished to sell for seventy-five dollars. It would have been a bargain, for as I learned afterwards such skins were then bringing three to four times that price in the market. However, I declined it whereupon she showed me a fine walrus tusk which she said her husband had given her and which she might therefore sell. At last I was interested and I asked her the price. She had none, but said she would take whatever Captain Cottle would say it was worth. I walked back posthaste to Captain Cottle, but when I put the question to him all that I could get from him was that it was worth what I would offer and what she would take. Again and again he made this statement. Back I was forced to go with nothing conclusive. I then offered two dollars for the tusk, with the understanding that if I found it was worth more than that I would pay her the additional amount the next time I was in Edgartown. She accepted my offer. The *Blue Wing* met me at the dock and as I stepped aboard I showed Vinal the tusk and asked him its value. He hefted it and said it weighed about ten pounds and was worth forty cents a pound. I made a mental note of the two dollars that I owed the woman.

The next summer when I happened again to be in Edgartown I walked to the cottage, knocked on the door, to have it opened by the woman herself. Before I could say anything she burst into a passion, informed me that her husband had told her she should never have sold the tusk, for it was a gift from him. She further said that she had heard nothing the whole winter but tusk-talk, that her husband was in the house then, and that if he knew who I was he would surely murder me. With that she slammed the door in my face, without giving me the opportunity to make amends of any kind. I went my way. A year later I was again in Edgartown and I called on Captain Cottle. How, I asked, are the whaler and his wife on Water Street? "Both in the graveyard," said Captain Cottle, and our conversation on that topic ended. Should I on my next trip to Edgartown bring the tusk with me, seek out the graves, and bury it with the couple in their last resting place? Our American Indians are said at the end of hostilities to bury the hatchet! Why not bury the tusk?

Joe Gardner, Mr. Perdum, and Vinal Edwards were all very helpful, each in his own way, to those of us who had undertaken research work at the Fisheries laboratory. All three were good examples of the kindly village folk of Woods Hole. I knew many others like and unlike them. For example Mrs. Eliott, Senior, a quiet, frail, almost delicate New England widow at whose house I roomed at one time. To look at her one would say that she was a product of the soil and had probably never ventured far from her present habitation, yet in her quiet way she once said to me that she had often sailed with her husband, who was a sea captain, that their son had been born, I believe, in Japan, and that she had been twice wrecked on the China coast. Such was Woods Hole!

For the first full season that I was at the Fisheries laboratory we had our living accommodations at the Fisheries residence, where we occupied sleeping rooms on the third floor and took our meals in a large dining room on the first floor. At that time the commissioner of fisheries was Colonel Marshall McDonald, who, with his family, occupied quarters on the second floor of the residence. The McDonalds, husband and wife, were generous, hospitable, southern people. Mrs. McDonald was a little formal, and for midday dinner we from the laboratory, superficially cleaned up, met in a drawing room next the dining room, and entered the latter on the arrival of the McDonalds. Mrs. McDonald sat at one end of the table, the Colonel at the other, and the rest of us between them. Our midday meal was a repast of excellent food cooked in southern style, ending usually with ice-cream. Generous hospitality was evident everywhere at the board. For our three meals daily and our sleeping quarters, we paid the Fisheries five dollars a week. Of course this small sum went much farther in those days than it would now, but I for one wondered how so much could be given us for so little. This was explained when the season closed and the mess account was found to have a deficit of about a thousand dollars. We were all much disturbed and told or wrote Colonel McDonald that, of course, we wished to reimburse him, but he declined our offers and we learned afterwards that the Fisheries found a way out of the difficulty without calling upon either us or the Colonel.

During the three summers that I worked at the Fisheries laboratory in Woods Hole, before I left for Europe in 1891, I met there a most interesting group of biologists. In addition to my old associates at the Philadelphia Academy of Natural Sciences, Dr. John A. Ryder and Dr. Spencer F. Trotter, I met Dr. Benjamin Sharp, then at the Academy; his enthusiasm for the European zoological laboratories, from which he had recently returned, whetted my appetite to have a firsthand acquaintance with these institutions. The Harvard laboratory was represented at Woods Hole by Dr. William Patten, H. H. Field, C. B. Davenport, and W. M. Woodworth. From Johns Hopkins came Professor W. K. Brooks and his students

Edwin Linten, R. P. Bigelow, F. H. Herrick, S. Watase, T. H. Morgan, E. G. Conklin, and H. V. Wilson; all of whom held important biological positions in later life. Princeton University was represented by Dr. C. F. McClure, the University of Indiana by Professor J. S. Kingsley, and Williams College by Professor S. F. Clarke. To meet these men, old and young, at our meals in the residence and about the laboratory was a biological education in itself. Play and work went on together.

The Marine Biological Laboratory was the second scientific center to establish itself in Woods Hole. It began operations in a single frame building in the summer of 1888 under the direction of its founder, Dr. C. O. Whitman. Its early years were passed under serious financial stress, but later under the direction of Dr. F. R. Lillie, its financial troubles ceased, for the most part, and it took on substantial and stable growth. After the first brick laboratory, the Crane Building, had been completed, several of us who had worked at the Fisheries were invited to transfer our research to this new situation. This I gladly did, for the facilities at the Marine Biological Laboratory were a great improvement over those at the Fisheries. Moreover, the summer classes at the Marine Biological kept a constant flow of the younger biologists through the institution, a feature which as Dr. Jacques Loeb once remarked, was as the breath of life to the laboratory. Thus this institution gradually outstripped the Fisheries as a situation for biological work, and with its final expansion it came to hold a place second to none in the seaside laboratories of the world. In its organization and in class-work and research it followed very closely the lines of Louis Agassiz's Penikese experiment. The breadth of Professor Agassiz's views in these matters is well illustrated by the following letter from him to the *New York Herald Tribune,* concerning the part to be played by physiology in such institutions.

NEW YORK, *June 14th, 1873*

MY DEAR SIR;

I read in this morning's Tribune a few remarks concerning Dr. Brown-Séquard and the Anderson School of Natural History on Penikese Island, which lead me to infer that some information concerning my plans for that institution may not be unwelcome to you. Natural History is no longer a mere descriptive science today.

It aims at improving knowledge by experiment as well as by observation. And from the first day I have known the intentions of Mr. Anderson, I have wished to combine physical and chemical experiments with the instruction and the work of research to be carried on at Penikese. That physiological experiments lay at the very foundation of an exhaustive study of Zoölogy is as plain as the simplest truth. But to do anything worth having in that direction, a master is needed at the head of the department and of course I thought at once of my old friend Brown-Séquard. Hearing of his intention to pay a visit this summer to his scientific friends in Europe, I felt that my hopes for the School were involved in his movements and I at once came to New-York determined to do my utmost to induce him to join me in laying the most solid foundation for the Anderson School. I have so far succeeded that my friend has promised me to give up his journey to Europe and stand by me until the School is fully organised and I know I shall have the sympathy of all the true friends of science in my success. Whether it will be possible for me to induce Dr. Brown-Séquard largely to forego for the present the advantages of medical practice to devote himself hereafter chiefly to physiological experiment, the future may decide. But what I rejoice in is the fact now settled that we shall have, in connection with the Anderson School, a physiological laboratory worthy of the high importance physiology has gained of late years in reference to medical science; and thus the School may extend the range of its usefulness in the application of science to the practical arts of modern civilisation.

With great regard

Yours very truly,

Ls. AGASSIZ

Wm. C. Wykoff, Esq.
Tribune Office
N. Y.

In the summer of 1918 I transferred my research work to the Marine Biological Laboratory, and from that time onward, with the omission of occasional seasons, I have spent my summers at this laboratory. Everyone who has worked there knows its liberal and generous policy, nor need anything be said of its magnificent library facilities and its supplies of apparatus. If marine biological work can be done anywhere, it can be done there. Some of my work on large dogfishes called for unusually large tanks and floating cages. These facilities were available in the newly opened Oceanographic Institute where, since 1932, I have had the use of large basement tanks and outside floats capable of keeping fishes three to four feet in length. Thus, by combining the facilities of both laboratories work could be carried out in Woods Hole that could scarcely be attempted elsewhere. Woods Hole has been described as the biologists' Mecca, but it is more than that, for its atmosphere is full of life. I once persuaded one of my good friends, Dean Clifford H. Moore, of the Harvard faculty, to spend a week or so of the summer at Woods Hole. Professionally, Dean Moore was a student and teacher of Latin, yet he entered fully into the spirit of our laboratory, watched our work, went on our excursions, listened to our seminars, lectures, and the like. When he was about to leave he summed up his impressions of biology at such a laboratory by saying: "If some activity in the study of the classics could be devised that would be the equivalent of the seaside laboratory for biology, the ancient languages would no longer be dead languages." It is in this respect that Woods Hole is more than a Mecca for a biologist.

The laboratory of the Woods Hole Oceanographic Institute is on the main street of the town and almost opposite the brick building of the Marine Biological Laboratory. The live dogfishes with which I was working one summer were received in the supply house of the Marine Biological Laboratory, and were then transferred across the street to the large sea water tanks in the basement of the Oceanographic laboratory. Early one morning an unusually fine, pregnant female dogfish arrived at the supply house and with my assistant, Miss Helen Porter, I proposed to carry the fish at once from the live-car, in which it had been transported, across the street to its final abode in the Oceanographic tank. The fish was perhaps four feet long and weighed well over fifteen pounds. I picked it up in my arms, holding the tail with one hand and the head with the other, and started on a mild run to cover as quickly as possible the four hundred feet or so between the two buildings. As I reached the street the fish began to give birth to her pups, each about a foot or so in length. These she dropped out one by one as I crossed the street. I looked back on my trail, now accentuated by squirming pups, to see Miss Porter, who had doubled up her laboratory apron, picking up one pup after another and putting it in the improvised carryall. I would have given anything for a snapshot of the two of us as we crossed the street, I ahead with the littering mother and Miss Porter behind with the newly arriving progeny. We reached the tank safely and deposited all in their proper, if not native, seawater and so far as we could see they were none the worse for their experience. As living fish they eventually served all their proper purpose. Miss Porter was certainly a most successful accoucheuse. Thus the Marine Biological Laboratory and the Oceanographic Institute coöperate in scientific work.

The Woods Hole laboratories, however all inclusive and unique they may be, are not the only laboratories on the western shores of the North Atlantic. Between Canada and Florida a number of such institutions have been established. One of the most inviting of these is the Bermuda biological station situated on the "still vex'd Bermoothes" some seven hundred miles east of the coast of the United States and in semi-tropical waters. This inviting situation for biological study seems to have been first pointed out by Professor A. E. Verrill of Yale University whose early studies on the fauna of the islands attracted the attention of biologists to the locality. Among these was Dr. Charles L. Bristol of New York University, who, about the close of the last century, took steps to found a biological station at Bermuda. This project was eventually taken over by Dr. E. L. Mark of Harvard who spent much energy and time in getting the station started, first on a temporary footing at the Frascati Hotel in Flatts Village, then at Agar's Island, and finally in well-established quarters a short distance from the old town of St. Georges. When the station was at the Frascati in 1905 Dr. Mark wishing to be free of its responsibilities for the season asked me to become its director; I accepted and was appointed for the period in question by the Harvard Corporation.

Previous to this time I had never been in Bermuda, and on my arrival there I was struck at once with its resemblance, so far as the sea was concerned, with the region about Naples. Its semi-tropical waters, marvelous in their shifting shades and colors, showed in their transparency a wealth of marine life on the bottom, an indescribable revelation to one who had been accustomed to work in the more northern seas. What are to be seen as dried or alcoholic specimens in collections were all here on the beaches or in the sea, alive and moving. Bermuda was a truly animated museum. We lived and worked at the Frascati Hotel on the inlet to Harrington Sound and about midway on the inside of the crescent of islets that make up Bermuda. The hotel was conducted by a Mr. Peniston of kindly but rigorous nature. There were a number of Penistons scattered over the islands but none, so he affirmed, was a relative of his. Such is true insularity! We had agreeable sleeping rooms in the Frascati. Fresh water was in those days scarce in Bermuda, and for tub-bathing we were allowed only four inches! There were rumors that in dry seasons fresh water had been sold in Bermuda for a shilling a bucket. For English, as for Americans, Providence did not favor the tub-bath. The Frascati gave us an ample but rather monotonous menu. Early one morning I heard the chef, Mr. Balch, call from below to Mr. Peniston to declare that the biologues had struck on too much hamlet, one of the most abundant marketable fishes in Bermuda. To this statement Mr. Peniston replied in an equally audible voice, "Well! give them hamlet but call it grouper."

One of my pleasures in going to Bermuda was that my wife could accompany me. She was as much transported by the beauty of the island as I was, and the work we were all doing then, rather of the old-fashioned, natural history kind, was more agreeable to her than what she had seen at Woods Hole where large quantities of fishes and other animals alive or semi-alive were to be seen everywhere. She made many agreeable acquaintances on the island, and the friendly way in which the Bermudians received her and the rest of our party added greatly to her enjoyment. We were as a group of visitors invited in many directions. We were told that Archdeacon Tucker, who lived near the Frascati, would wish to have us to tea some afternoon, but that for the moment he could not well do so, for he was about to move to his summer residence. Finally his invitation came and we all spent a most delightful afternoon on an island in Harrington Sound where he and his family had gone for the summer. What surprised us most was that the archdeacon's summer migration consisted in going from the shore of Harrington Sound where he lived in the winter to an island in the sound a mile or so off. This passage, however, seemed to mean as much to the Tucker family as a summer transfer of a Bostonian to the California coast. The same was true all over Bermuda. There were people living in St. Georges who had never gone nor apparently ever expected to go to Hamilton, the rival town, some ten miles away, and we were told that some of the inhabitants of St. David's Island, at most a mile or two long, had never in all their lives been off this small plot of land. Such are the limitations of life!

My wife's pleasure in Bermuda was marred only by her frequent touches of paratyphoid. The islands were at that time full of paratyphoid, the germs of which were probably carried in the dust. Many of us who in the first part of our stay there suffered from this malady, evidently developed an immunity to it, for we were later free of it. My wife, however, continued to suffer from it to the end of her visit. It is remarkable that shortly after she boarded the steamer for New York, the fever abated and even before she reached the states she was almost well. Evidently she was continuously and inconveniently reinfected as long as she was on the islands. I am glad to say that as a result of modern hygiene paratyphoid has completely disappeared from Bermuda, and that judging from my recent visits there, the island is now a most wholesome spot.

But to return to the Bermuda laboratory. The Frascati had several small outside buildings and these we were allowed to use for our work. All these buildings were on the slope of land next the inlet from which we carried the sea water for our aquaria. Each of the score of workers at the laboratory had his or her own task. Some were gathering and preparing specimens for college or museum collections. One of our number, Professor Trevor Kincaid from Washington University on the Pacific coast, was most industrious in accumulating specimens. We landed from the New York steamer in Hamilton, whence we were to be transported by bus over four or five miles of sunny road to the Frascati. Scarcely had we arrived from New York when Kincaid rushed to a dry goods shop on Front Street in Hamilton and purchased a large, flat pasteboard box which he had mostly filled with pinned insects caught from the bus by net as we drove to the Frascati. Many more were added to his collection in the late afternoon and all was left on his laboratory table over night. The next morning only a few wings and legs of his collection were to be found, for the Bermuda ants had been there in myriads during the night and had devoured or removed most of what Kincaid had brought together. The next day's work was suspended for security by cords from the ceiling instead of standing on a table, but the ants used the cords as bridges and again ruined most of the collection. Finally all specimens were put on a large table the legs of which stood in saucers of kerosene, and this time man won out over the insect.

Some of us had come to Bermuda with particular problems in mind. Dr. E. G. Conklin and I both wished to work on a small fish-like creature, known as amphioxus, which is found in the coral sand banks of the shallow waters of Bermuda. Conklin was interested in the embryology of this creature and I in its sensory activities. We soon found that it was known to the small colored boys in the neighborhood, and that one of these youngsters in particular, known as "Doctor" Gilbert, was very successful in its capture. Conklin and I engaged him to supply us with what he called "amfiroxen" and we paid him, I believe, a penny apiece for fresh, active specimens. Usually he would bring to us each morning two jars of sea water with half his morning's catch in each. We thus ordinarily had plenty of the creatures at our disposal. At times, however, the catch would drop off and then I would get all on a given day and Conklin all on the next and so on. Finally a week went by during which I received none, though I saw Gilbert carry a jar often to Conklin's laboratory. I asked one of Gilbert's companions, whom I happened to meet and who seemed concerned about talking with me, why I had not seen Gilbert with his supplies of amphioxus. He said: "Oh! don't you know?" I protested I did not. I then extracted from him a confession. He said Dr. Conklin asked Gilbert if he had ever seen Dr. Parker with his shoes off, to which he got a negative answer. Dr. Conklin then said to Gilbert: "Do you know that he has cloven feet?" That was enough for Gilbert! From that moment on he shunned me and my ways. I then made it a point to walk about in my bare feet, and I soon found that the colored boys no longer avoided me. In fact, after a short while Gilbert was bringing me amphioxus as usual. I admitted to Conklin that he knew negro psychology better than I did, but in the end I had the laugh on him, for my specimens of amphioxus gave me very good sensory reactions and I finished an interesting piece of research, whereas Conklin, I regret to say, never once during the whole season got his creatures to lay for him a single egg. Thus adventures in biological research sometimes yield sweet revenge.

It must be evident from even this brief sketch how very important seaside laboratories are to the biologist. That even the oldest of these institutions should date from within less than a century ago shows something of the handicap under which the older naturalists must have worked. It is therefore not surprising that their knowledge of marine life was in so many respects insufficient and even erroneous. The establishment of laboratories on the oceanic shores, and especially on large, ocean-going vessels, opened an entirely new vista to those workers whose knowledge led them to the geographical source of living things. How quickly many of these older investigators seized upon the idea, and how broadly they proposed to develop it, is well seen in the letter quoted in this chapter from Louis Agassiz about his Penikese venture.

XVII

Academic Advancements and Counting Seals

AT NOON THE ANCIENT OF THE SEA HIMSELF (PROTEUS) CAME FORTH
AND FOUND HIS FAT SEALS AND WENT DOWN THE LINE OF THEM TO ADD
UP THEIR NUMBER.

T. E. Shaw, The Odyssey of Homer

IT might seem that academic advancements and counting seals
are in no way connected, but in my case the relation was most intimate as I shall hope to show. My academic progress, from the time
of my first appointment as instructor in zoology at Harvard University in 1888, was unusually slow. I was told that this was the
policy of President Eliot: giving younger appointees a thorough
tryout before advancing them. My academic standing of instructor
was not changed to that of assistant professor till 1899, eleven years
after my first appointment. It is true, however, that when I first
became instructor at Harvard I was the youngest teacher of that
grade in the college, and it is also true that two of the eleven years
mentioned were spent abroad on a Harvard fellowship; nevertheless the period of my novitiate was a long one, and in my opinion
an unduly long one. With a readjustment in the department in
1899 I was invited to undertake new responsibilities, and was
given my first real advancement. Yet during this very early period
of my teaching association with Harvard I had several excellent
calls to go to other institutions. It was a pleasure to carry with me
when I first went to Europe, as a student, a letter from President
David Starr Jordan offering me a teaching position in zoology at
the newly established Leland Stanford University in California.
It gave me a certain sense of security, and yet I finally declined it
in favor of Harvard. Within the next dozen years I had some six
such invitations from as many universities or colleges, the last one
in 1906 from Professor Russell H. Chittenden who asked me to

take charge of the Yale zoological laboratory. I naturally called on President Eliot to talk over the situation with him. He had already heard of the offer and asked at once: "And what does Mrs. Parker say to this proposal?" I told him that she wished to stay in Cambridge. He then said: "I believe you will stay here and I shall be glad to do what I can to make that stay agreeable to Mrs. Parker and to you." He then made a very generous proposal to me under the provisions of which I worked with satisfaction till I became emeritus. Thus all my teaching appointments in Harvard, from assistant in my senior year in 1886 to professor twenty years later, came from the hand of President Eliot.

In June 1906 the Harvard Co-operative Society, where I had long done most of my personal shopping, held a clearance sale of men's apparel. My wife knowing that I needed a new hat advised me to buy one at the cooperative and put it aside till autumn when it could be brought out and used. The stiff, black derby was the common style in those days and I purchased a good hat of this kind, and at a very reasonable price. In the autumn when I put it on it dropped down to my ears, though in June it seemed a good fit. I was nonplused, but my wife brought me to my senses by remarking: "Don't you remember? You were made *full* professor in June." I wore the hat that winter, but I was obliged to have considerable extra lining put inside the band for I discovered by daily experience that the full professor, after all, was not so different from other members of the faculty.

During this period of slow academic advancement I was received into quite a number of scientific societies, both in this country and abroad, and served on some of them in various official capacities. Two of these societies, among the later ones to grant me membership, were the American Philosophical Society in my native town of Philadelphia, which elected me a member in 1911, and the National Academy of Sciences of Washington which admitted me two years later. Admission to these bodies was a source of great gratification to me. In the National Academy in those days it was a rule for members to send a congratulatory telegram to a newly elected associate, on his admission to the body. On the day of my election to the Academy I received such a message signed by nine of my colleagues. I have kept this bit of kindly information as evidence of how the Morse code can disguise a dispatch. My telegram read

"War congratulations Ejection National Academy." Yet I was pleased rather than disturbed by this message!

It is a fact often forgotten that the National Academy of Sciences, which came into being in 1863 under President Lincoln, was established as a scientific advisory body to the United States government. In pursuance of this capacity I was nominated by the then president of the Academy, Dr. W. H. Welch, the year after I became a member, to be one of three investigators to proceed to the Pribilof Islands in the Bering Sea to report to the federal authorities on the number and condition of the government fur seals on these islands. Thus my election to one of the most distinguished scientific bodies in the land brought me at once into a responsible position for counting seals.

When the United States acquired the whole of Alaska, through purchase from Russia negotiated by Secretary Seward in 1867, it received as part of its purchase the Pribilof Islands, two small volcanic dots of land some twenty miles apart and near the center of the Bering Sea. They are known as the islands of St. Paul and St. George. Here, and on a few nearby rocky islets, each summer congregate all the American fur seals for their annual breeding season. Such a complete and universal seasonal gathering of one species of animal for breeding is probably not known anywhere else in the world. In the early days of the Russian explorers in the north Pacific, some hundred and fifty years ago, navigators noticed great numbers of fur seals migrating northward from the Pacific Ocean, through the passes between the Aleutian Islands, and into the Bering Sea. Their destination was not known till Pribilof, a Russian explorer, followed them to the island of St. George in 1786. Subsequently, many of the seals were found to go on to St. Paul, and thus their two breeding places were identified. These two islands became the very lucrative centers for the sealing activities of the Russians, till they passed into the possession of the United States. Our government then leased the sealing privileges, under restrictions, to the Alaska Commercial Company for twenty years, from 1870 to 1890, and then again for another twenty years to the North American Commercial Company. The seal herds having shown a dangerous reduction in numbers toward the close of the last century, the government of the United States undertook for itself the business of sealing, and beginning shortly after 1910 the whole management of the Pribilof seal herds was in its hands, where it still remains.

To understand what the situation was when three of us were asked to go to the Pribilofs to count and report on the seals, something must be said about the natural history of these animals. First of all the seals that congregate on the Pribilofs each summer are fur seals, not the ordinary hair seals, and possess a pelt that in fineness and softness far exceeds that of most other animals. It is, in fact, one of the most highly prized furs in the market. On the beaches of the Pribilofs in any given year the first seals to appear arrive in the late spring or early summer. They are the breeding males or bulls, large, vigorous, active creatures weighing some 400 pounds each. They take their positions on parts of the rocky beaches regularly occupied by seals, and known as rookeries, and defend their local claims by vigorously fighting off all later intruding bulls. The bulls are soon followed, usually early in June, by the females or cows. These are relatively small in size weighing at most 80 pounds. Thus they are about one-fifth the weight of a bull, a sexual disparity seen in very few other higher animals. When a cow first comes out of the sea she enters with apparent indifference the family group, or harem, of a given bull. Here she is held by the bull for a week or more till she has given birth to the one young, or pup, that she carries after which she goes into heat, pairs with the bull and a new pup is started while she is giving milk to the pup recently born. Thus the period of gestation for the fur seal is a little less than a year, and in one way or another the cow has one or two pups with her most of the time. After she has become pregnant the bull will allow her to reënter the sea, feed, and return to his harem, for her newly born pup is left there and she comes back to give it milk with evident solicitude. When a given harem is fully formed, as is likely to occur in mid-July, it consists of a bull, with his associated cows, perhaps thirty or forty in number, and an equal number of newly born pups. Each bull rules his own harem as an autocrat, and will permit no cow to return to the sea till she is impregnated, nor will he allow a newly arrived bull to enter his preserves and possibly steal from him one of his as yet unfertilized cows. Eternal vigilance is the price of family integrity, and this the bull gives his harem from the time this aggregate begins to form till breeding is completed. Thus for two to three months the bull stands on continuous guard day and night without food and without water. The result is that the breeding bull which starts the season as a powerful, vigorous, vindictive creature who will chase a man for fifty feet if he comes too near its harem, ends the season a bag of skin and bones with scarcely strength enough to drag himself about.

Cows begin breeding when they are a couple of years old, but the males do not take part in this activity till they are some three times that age. The young non-breeding males are called bachelors and herd more or less by themselves in special areas on the rookeries, the bachelors' hauling grounds. As the breeding season wanes some of the older bachelors make their way in among the groups of harems and steal newly arrived, late cows and carry them off. In this way they start a small harem of their own and gradually in a few years make a place for themselves among the breeding bulls. At the height of the season the rookeries are the scenes of the utmost confusion and are permeated by a characteristic odor noticeable for a distance of a mile or more. The bulls hissing, snorting, and bellowing, the cows calling in sheep-like bleats to their pups, and the pups responding in a higher pitch all contribute to a bedlam of noise which deafens the visitor and has to be experienced to be appreciated. Into this malodorous tumult and confusion the fur seal pup is born, and yet from the beginning he seems to be quite at home. He certainly thrives under conditions of filth where most animals would be expected to perish outright. His habits are extremely playful. He is continually rolling about and tugging and pulling at his companions. If an observer stoops down in a group of pups coat tails and trouser legs are likely to be seized and pulled by these little creatures in a way that is wholly pup-like, and the appropriateness of the name becomes at once evident. Till early in August the pups remain strictly on shore, after which they begin to take to the water, first paddling and then swimming. Thus they start their preparation for the winter migration when, as plump little seals with a weight varying from twenty-five to fifty pounds each, they desert their birthplace for the open water. By late summer the breeding is entirely over, the harems are disintegrated, and in early autumn the spent bulls, the cows and their pups with the rest of the herd take to the sea for a long southern migration. The beaches are now entirely deserted of seals and the herd moves into the open north Pacific to lead a free, ocean life till its return the next spring to the island rookeries. And so runs the year of the fur seal herd.

After the discovery of the breeding grounds of the Alaskan fur seals by the Russian navigators the herd from time to time suffered serious depletions from which, however, recovery was always made as a result of restrictive killing. A serious diminution in the size of the herd was reached under American management at the beginning of this century. On investigation it was declared that this diminution was due chiefly to pelagic sealing. This kind of sealing was carried on in the open sea in summer and far enough away from the Pribilof Islands to be legal. It resulted, however, in the killing of large numbers of cow seals, for these were the class of seal in the open sea at that season. The killing of a cow seal at that time of year was most destructive to the herd, for it meant not only her loss, but the loss of the unborn pup in her body and the death by starvation of her newly born pup temporarily left by her in the rookery on the beach. Those who practiced pelagic sealing were chiefly American, British, and Japanese sealers. After a conference of representatives of these three nations in Washington, D. C., it was agreed to make pelagic sealing illegal for the nationals of these countries and to give the herd a chance to recuperate if pelagic sealing was the cause of the reduction in numbers. The annual count of seals as made by the government agents on the two seal islands consequently came to be a matter of great moment. After this enumeration had been in force it was claimed on the floor of Congress, by those who disbelieved that pelagic sealing was accountable for the diminution of the herd, that the reported numbers for the herd made by the island agents were falsified and that the favorable signs seen in the claimed increase of the herd on the cessation of pelagic sealing was fictitious. President Wilson was therefore authorized to send three investigators to the seal islands in 1914 to make an impartial count of the seals and to report back to Congress. The persons selected for this undertaking were Mr. W. O. Osgood, nominated by the Smithsonian Institution, Mr. E. A. Preble, nominated by the United States Department of Agriculture, and myself, nominated by the National Academy of Sciences. Shortly after the organization of the group we met in Washington with Mr. W. C. Redfield, secretary of the Department of Commerce, for a general conference. The outcome of this meeting was a request on the part of the secretary that he wished a report returned by us which we all could agree upon, and not a split report with each one expressing his own views. As our report was to turn mainly on an enumeration of seals it seemed to me that the secretary's admonition savored rather of politics than of scientific integrity, for we all three entertained no doubts about our ability to count and to tell the truth. Before we started on our way to the Pribilofs we learned that we were to have companion investigators from the other nations concerned: from Great Britain Mr. James M. Macoun of the Geological Survey of Canada and Mr. B. W. Harmon of the Dominion Department of Marine and Fisheries, and from Japan, Dr. T. Kitahara of the Imperial Japanese Fisheries Bureau. Thus the party totaled six, and while the three from the United States were the official reporting members it may be said here in anticipation that not only these three but all six of the party signed the enumerations of seals reported, a conclusion which marks the difference between what a politician may anticipate as the outcome of an effort and what reputable scientists may contribute to it.

To me the whole expedition was an education for I had never in my life been west of Chicago. The three of us from the United States went directly by train to Seattle where we met the revenue cutter *McCulloch,* under the command of Captain P. H. Uberroth. On this vessel we, with our two Canadian associates, left for the Pribilofs on June 11 and arrived at our destination on June 21. The north Pacific Ocean is not an exciting part of the world. From the time we lost sight of land on our west coast till we sighted the Aleutian Islands at Unimak Pass we saw not a single sail. Life on shipboard was, however, not monotonous. The *McCulloch* was light and she rolled freely. We had sleeping quarters in the captain's cabin, Osgood had a floor bunk on the left side of the cabin and I had a similar one on the right some fifteen feet apart. We turned in one night in quiet weather and each put his clothes on a chair next his bunk. During the night a terrific gale arose and the cutter rolled so heavily that it took all my strength to keep from being tossed out of my bunk. In the dark I heard the chair with my clothes fall over on the floor and the same happened to Osgood's. As the ship rolled the mass of our combined clothing and the two chairs would slide across the cabin floor and hit first the base of my bunk and then that of Osgood's. I began to wonder what would be left of our apparel. As the morning light broke faintly Osgood and I tried to dress. When the pile of clothes was on his side of the cabin he would reach out from his bunk and seize what he believed to be the next piece of clothing needed in his dressing, and when on the next roll my turn came I tried the same. Gradually, in the course of an hour or so, we got enough clothes on to get out of our bunks and chase the remaining pieces from one side of the cabin to the other until we got ourselves fairly covered. We finally found that we had put on clothes that belonged to the appropriate person though considering the circumstances of our dressing it was a wonder! Osgood and I were the first up, but there was nothing doing. Our Portuguese cabin boy was nowhere to be found. As day came we took our chances on deck, succeeded in making the galley, and there had some hot coffee and toast which the cook said would have to serve for breakfast till the gale blew itself out. Captain Uberroth slept through the whole affair. He was a real seaman. Three of our party were desperately seasick and kept to their hammocks or bunks. Osgood and I confessed that we had never in our lives been through such a sea experience. We were glad to run into quiet weather by noon.

An interesting experience that we had every few days on the *McCulloch* was watching the special order for the day. Toward the middle of the afternoon of a given day we would see Captain Uberroth put on his belt and pistols, step out on deck, and in a loud voice shout out the special order which was a practice order for the crew. The order would be Fire, Abandon Ship, Clear for Action or some such command. This was then whistled by the vessel's steam whistle that everyone should know what the order was. The officers would then take their places on deck, the crew would break into squads and run to position, and whatever had been ordered would be carried out as quickly as possible. The squad that was earliest to respond in completeness to the order got a credit mark which was of importance to them in promotions. When Fire was called the squad that got the first stream of water overboard received the credit mark. Each squad worked with feverish excitement during which the water in the hose flew in many directions. On several occasions I saw young officers standing in position doused with salt water from head to foot as the hose was handled without too much skill. I asked one of these unfortunates what happened to the squad which thus soaked an officer. He smiled and said: "Nothing happens to them, it all happens to us." It is one of the few ways in which a common seaman can get even with an unpopular superior. Most of the officers in the service were fine fellows, but before I was through with revenue cutters for the season I met some whom I too would willingly have soused.

After about ten days at sea we noticed floating weed, then sighted the Cape, Scotch Cap, at the entrance to Unimak Pass in the Aleutian Islands, through which we set our course into the Bering Sea. It was wonderful to see land again, and such land. On the Alaskan side of the pass stood the two volcanoes, Shishaldin and Isanotski, the snow-capped smoking peaks of which rose some fifteen thousand feet above the sea. We stopped for a day at Dutch Harbor, for mail and other information, and then entered the Bering Sea to pass the island of St. George in the fog and to arrive in fairly clear weather at St. Paul in the late afternoon of June 21.

The island of St. Paul, like that of its brother island, St. George, is without a harbor. We and our belongings were landed at an open, stone wharf and from there we walked the quarter of a mile or so into the native village. This consisted of about two or three wide lanes with rows of one story three room frame houses arranged in orderly sequence. The government house and the store toward which we went were double-decked frame constructions. Not a soul was to be seen. We were somewhat surprised, but we at last found a man at the government house who told us that the whole village had gone to the carpenter shop, the largest building there, to see the first moving picture show which had ever come to the island. A few days before our arrival a United States naval vessel had put in to set in order the new radio station just then erected for the island. This vessel carried a portable moving-picture outfit, and as a special and novel treat to the natives this outfit had been brought on the island and all in the village had been invited to come to the show. Hence the absence of life about the settlement. We dropped our bags at the government house and went in a body to the carpenter shop. The population of the village of St. Paul was then a little fewer than two hundred, and this whole congregation was crowded together into the carpenter shop to see the pictures.

We were evidently in time to view most of the film, which consisted largely of views of New York with vessels in the harbor, sky-scrapers, crowded street scenes, Central Park views, railroad trains on the elevated and on the surface, all of which seemed very familiar to us. At the end of the show the native chief was brought to us and introduced. He was an intelligent, well-dressed man of middle age who had been elected by the other natives on the island to his post and who spoke simple English. After having met us he turned to those in the shop, told them in the Aleut language who we were, and then asked us if we wished to speak to the villagers or ask anything of them. I was pushed forward and spoke a few words of greeting which were translated by the chief into Aleut, and then I asked him what had been of most interest to the villagers in the movie which they had just looked at. There was much buzzing consultation, after which he said they were most interested to see that trees moved in the wind and that their branches were not stiff and rigid as they had heretofore thought. We then learned that there were no trees on the island, that, in fact, the nearest trees were at Dutch Harbor some hundred miles away and that few or none of the natives had ever been off St. Paul. The only trees that they ever had seen were occasional trunks with a few stiff, leafless branches on them which had been washed from the Alaskan mainland to their island. Thus we began to learn the psychology of this isolated, Russian-Aleut, half-breed population.

The school teacher on the island, a very intelligent American who, with his wife, did what they could for the welfare of the natives, complained of the circumstances under which he had to work. He told us that the United States government sent him a stock of primers to use in his school in which a picture of an object was given and below it its name in English. There would be a picture of a dog, with the name dog spelled out below, one of a tree again with the name below, a horse, a cow, and so on. "But what am I to do with such a book," asked he, "when not one of these things exists on the island? It is not surprising," he said, "to hear the natives complain of the English language as a very impractical one, because in learning it they are expected to remember so many things which they never have seen." I asked him what he regarded as the outcome of his three or four years of teaching, and he said sorrowfully that it amounted to bringing the pupil to the point of saying yes or no to very simple questions that might be asked of him. When I looked at the educational problem that this poor man had to face day in and day out I felt that my difficulties in trying to teach Harvard students, bad as the results commonly were, amounted to nothing compared with those of my distant colleague on the Pribilofs. Yet how depressing Harvard College sometimes is! I was once showing a laboratory section in elementary zoology through the rooms of fossils in the Agassiz Museum. We were in the palaeozoic room, where some of the most ancient fossils known were exhibited, and I remarked that some of these fragments were the remains of animals alive some five hundred million years ago. I tried to impress on the minds of the students what an enormous amount of time five hundred million years is, and I tried to illustrate with comparison to the probable one million of years during which man may be said to have been on the earth; one innocent queried my five hundred million statement by asking: "A.D. or B.C.?" I nearly collapsed, but as I looked at the faces of most of the members of the section and saw the broad smiles there, I said in the blackness of my heart: "Probably B.C." No further question was asked, and the inquirer continued to write as though satisfied. As a teacher of Harvard students I would at that moment have sold out to the lowest bidder!

To return to the Pribilofs: we settled in the village of St. Paul at the government house and began to watch the coming of the bulls on Gorbatch Rookery, the nearest rookery to the village. In all there were about a dozen rookeries on St. Paul but we could know what was occurring on all of them by watching Gorbatch, the one nearest at hand. This occupied about half a mile of very stony beach and day by day more bulls took positions on it. Soon the cows began to appear, and shortly after that we saw the first pups born. Soon after the middle of July we assumed that all the breeding bulls had arrived and we began to count them. This was an easy undertaking for the bulls kept their places on the beach, were large, conspicuous creatures, and lifted themselves well above the other seals. It was like counting telegraph-poles as one walks along a telegraph line. All six of us walked together along the bluff above Gorbatch and counted, one by one, the breeding bulls, agreeing on a total of 112. In about a week we had thus counted all the breeding bulls in the twelve rookeries on St. Paul and in the six on St. George and obtained a grand total of 1,559, an enumeration probably accurate to within one or two percent. A week or so later we essayed counting the pups. At this time in the summer, about the end of July, the cows can be easily driven into the sea, the bulls will remain at their old locations, and the pups are strong enough to be herded to one end of a given rookery. From this region they can then be allowed to return to the rookery in narrow files and can be counted as they pass, a pair of enumerators for each file. This count cannot be so accurate as the count of bulls, but it must be very close. Gorbatch Rookery yielded 6,152 pups, and the count for both St. Paul and St. George gave a grand total of 93,250. There is every reason to believe that each cow gives birth to one, and not more than one, pup a year. Sterile cows are very rare and twin pups have never been recorded. Hence the number of pups born in any year must be the measure of the number of cows in that year. Thus all the classes of animals in the fur seal herds were accounted for except the bachelors and maturing but non-breeding bulls. These were roughly counted and estimated and yielded a total of 106,456. So the enumeration of the fur seal herd, which might seem at first sight an insoluble problem, was at last accomplished and with a grand total of about 294,000 individuals. This total figure confirmed the enumerations of the keepers on the islands for previous years and showed that, contrary to what had been said from the floor of Congress, the herd, now that pelagic sealing had almost entirely been eliminated, was increasing and that the increase was such as to warrant the expectation of a rapid recovery. This expectation has been fully realized, for the total herd of fur seals which numbered somewhat over a quarter of a million in 1914 is now, in 1943, estimated as some two and three-quarter millions. The enumeration of the Pribilof fur seals for 1914 having been completed, I left the islands on the revenue cutter *Tahoma* which picked me up at St. Paul on August 6 and started me on my return trip home by way of California.

XVIII

The Pacific Gold Coast

GOLD! GOLD! GOLD! GOLD!
BRIGHT AND YELLOW, HARD AND COLD.
T. Hood

THE Pacific Northwest, at least in the summer of 1914, was in many respects an isolated region. On the Pribilof Islands news from the outside world was gathered almost exclusively from the radio station. Here, each evening for about a quarter of an hour, the headlines of the day were to be heard. In this way, early in August, we learned of the breaking out of the first World War. We scarcely believed our ears, but as details continued to come day by day we were at length convinced that a European war had actually begun. The island radio was officially limited to government business, but it was understood before we left the states that in case of serious illness, either to any of us on the islands or to those in our homes, word would be sent in either direction, and that no word was good word. During the summer letters from the mainland reached us only some three times. After the count of the seals was completed the revenue cutter *Tahoma* on August 6, as already mentioned, carried three of us out into the Bering Sea where we were to meet the Nome-Seattle steamer *Senator* on her way south. We got in touch with the *Senator*, first by radio and then by whistle, for we were, as is usual for the Bering Sea, in dense fog, and I and several other passengers with our luggage were transferred by boat to the liner. Now it seemed that we were really headed for the states! The *Senator*, however, was not making a direct run to Seattle, but was conducting a summer excursion tour with several stops at Alaskan ports. We were to make brief calls at Seward, at Valdez, and at Cordova after which we were to proceed directly to Seattle.

The *Senator* was an antiquated ocean liner that plied between Nome and our Pacific coast as far south as San Francisco. She was provided with simple staterooms to which water, hot or cold, was brought in pitchers. She was without bathtubs or showers, a disappointment to us, for during the whole summer on the islands we had washed in basins of hot water which were given us with some reluctance by the Chinese cook in the government house. Fresh water was scarce on the island of St. Paul and not much more abundant on St. George.

Almost all the passengers on the *Senator* were from the vicinity of Nome, or at least from the Yukon. Gold was their one theme. In the stateroom next to mine were two gold miners who kept on one of their bunks, in full view from the passageway, all their gold-washings done up in skin bags. During our whole voyage one or other of these men sat guard, revolver in hand, over their hoard. By relieving each other, this continuous vigil was strictly kept, day and night, and in this way they protected their store of yellow metal till they reached port. Bright and yellow, hard and cold! Their cabin door was always open, but no one was ever invited to enter. What a life! To them the whole world seemed ready to pounce upon their hard-earned gains. They were on their way to one of the gold banks in San Francisco. Another product of the gold fields was a decrepit, broken-down Irishman who in wretched clothes hobbled about the decks and passageways of the steamer. He made no trouble and seemed to be thankful to go unnoticed. The captain of the *Senator* told us that this poor wretch had been some fifteen years in the gold fields, had never had anything but hard luck, and was finally reduced to earning his bread by cutting firewood for camps. Rheumatism or something like it had finally seized him and he became quite incapacitated. The captain had taken him aboard at Nome and begged money enough from the passengers to pay the old fellow's way to San Francisco where he claimed he had relatives who would care for him.

During meals on shipboard I sat at a small table with a family of three, father, mother, and full-grown son, all of whom had spent some ten years or more in working a Yukon claim that had yielded them a steady flow of gold. This they had sent year by year to a San Francisco bank where they now knew that a reasonable competence for their old age awaited them. The wife, who sat next to me at table, was a frank, honest, hard-working soul of American extraction who looked on their Alaskan adventure as a success. She had kept house, if living in a log cabin can be called that, and had cooked the meals for her two men as they worked their claim. She had bought herself a new calico dress before leaving Alaska and she took great pleasure in wearing it. Her great trial was the bill of fare at dinner. Mostly in French terms it puzzled her greatly, and she finally came to rely upon me largely to help her order her meals. Her two men ignored the bill of fare completely and told the steward in simple English what they wanted, and usually got it. The father described to me the way he and his son worked their claim and brought home their gold day by day. They always carried guns with them and when they saw poachers on their preserves they took steps that as a rule quickly persuaded the invaders to move on. On one occasion they noticed three men working on the lower part of their claim. They at once ordered them off, but the three put up such a hard-luck tale and begged to work there for only a few days to get out enough gold to pay their way back to the states, that they were allowed to stay. A week or so later my informant said he saw all three men down the river at a camp, roaring drunk, and boasting about the way they had done an old fellow farther up country out of a good pocket of gold by wholesale lying. Lying, stealing, drinking, and killing, what cannot be laid at the feet of the Mammon Gold?

The *Senator* made her three Alaskan stops in sequence: Seward, Valdez, and Cordova. As we approached each town, irrespective of the hour, our vessel blew a long, heavy blast from her whistle and by the time we were at the wharf the whole population in the settlement was out to welcome us. At Seward we were met by real-estate scalpers. It was then rumored that the new Alaskan railroad was to start from Seward, and it was believed that every lot of land in town would rise in price three or four times on notice that the railroad terminal was to be located there. But there was more than this. The land agent who singled me out told me that a certain well-conditioned house which he pointed out to me from the dock, had been built on a lot the owner of which, before he built, panned the top soil and got enough gold out of it to pay for the ground. I told the retailer of this wonderful story that I had never heard of gold in Seward. He confessed that none was known there, but that the lot in question had been for some years the sight of the chief barroom in Seward where the miners from the back country in early days paid for drinks and gambled with gold-dust. In the various exchanges more or less of the precious metal was continually dropping on the floor where it fell through the cracks onto the soil beneath and thus reached a new resting place. The buyer of the lot knew this and knew it to his advantage, for the price of his lot was already awaiting him in its top earth. Notwithstanding this and sundry other tempting offers I resisted buying any Seward real estate.

At Cordova the dock was a short distance from town, but near the wharf and nailed to two trees was a broad, unfinished board carrying the enigmatic legend "The Stampede, Any Meal 50 Cents." A Texas farmer, who had never been out of his state before and who was taking the Alaskan excursion on the *Senator* saw the sign, told me that he had paid a dollar apiece for every meal he had eaten in Alaska, and that fifty cents was the proper Texan price for any real repast. He said that he proposed to hunt up "The Stampede" and to have dinner there. I met him as we were returning to the boat and I asked him if he had found "The Stampede." He was full of praise for this Cordovan eating house. He told me that all diners sat at one large table on which the food freshly prepared in the kitchen was placed on large platters or in deep bowls and, to use his expression, "You just slipped back your ears and slipped in." Why the Texan preferred to pay half a dollar for this kind of meal when another was awaiting him and already paid for on the boat I did not learn, but there is no accounting for tastes. From Cordova the *Senator* steered into the northern Pacific and took an open ocean course for the strait of Juan de Fuca and Seattle, where we arrived toward the end of August. I remained long enough at the Washington Hotel in Seattle to have three hot, tub-baths one after the other, to get my hair and beard properly trimmed, for I had not been under a barber's care for almost three months, and to buy a through railroad ticket to Berkeley, California, where my wife was awaiting me.

Our reunion at Berkeley was indeed a happy occasion, for I had not seen my wife nor really heard from her, except in a most fragmentary way, in some three months. Neither of us had ever been in California before so that we looked forward to an exciting if brief visit to this state of immeasurable prospects. From Berkeley we made a few days' excursion into the Yosemite Valley and to the

Mariposa Grove of Big Trees. It was the dry season and the roads into the valley were thick with a powdery dust. When we arrived at Camp Curry on the floor of the valley what we most needed was a thorough dusting and shower bath, but we were obliged to content ourselves with the familiar substitute of pitchers of water and basins. The absence of shower baths reminded me of a treacherous discovery that my old friend Winthrop Osterhout made in this very place and as a result of trying to solve the bathing problem. He was then a member of the Berkeley faculty and was given to camping in the Yosemite. The chief deficiency in such a recreation, if there is such a thing as a deficiency in California, was the absence of a shower bath. To remedy this, Osterhout had the bright idea of bringing with him to the valley a large horse sponge. In the early morning and with a very slight amount of covering on him he carried his sponge to the bank of the Merced River, saturated it with pure glacial water, and holding it on his head pressed it till a wonderful deluge of cool fluid streamed down over him. After two or three such douches he was fit as a fiddle and the one defect of the Yosemite seemed to be a matter of the past. But not so! The sponge was put behind the camp and the next morning the operation was repeated. When, however, the sponge gorged with Merced water was again squeezed overhead, not only did water descend upon the would-be bather, but also a thousand earthworms, bugs, centipedes, slugs, and the like, all of which during the night had been attracted into the sponge by its dampness. Needless to say that this ended the glorious discovery, but the results were probably not without their good effect, for in time running water was introduced into most of the valley camps.

The enjoyment of the Yosemite comes from living with it, scaling its walls, seeking out its waterfalls, sleeping on its floor, and making the acquaintance of its neighborhood. We took a day's trip into the Mariposa Grove of Big Trees, the heights of which may reach beyond three hundred feet and the ages of which will carry some trees well before the Christian Era. Surfeited more or less with this native grandeur and the beauty of the valley we made our way back to Berkeley by train along the banks of the Merced, the soil and stones of which were still piled as the miners had left them after their wild hunt for the last flakes of the precious metal in 1849 and later. We stayed long enough in Berkeley to become well acquainted with its surroundings, the superb view out through the Golden Gate with Mount Tamelpeis to the north, the whole panorama of San Francisco to the south, and the great bay at the foot of all.

Chinatown in San Francisco held me in thrall. In a little shop on Grant Avenue I was enamored of a shrine bell beautifully but simply carved in wood. It looked like a gigantic half-opened clam, and it was meant to lie near a household shrine and be sounded with a wooden knocker by anyone who wished the attention of the gods. It was exquisitely shaped, and had, as I afterwards found out, a beautifully oaken tone. My wife said, "One more thing to dust," and I passed it by, but its shape and music continued to haunt me. When, two years later, we were again in San Francisco and together walked through Grant Avenue, imagine my surprise on seeing my bell still unsold and hanging in the same shop window. Without further ado I bought it and for years it was a part of my curio collection at home, till I found it meant so much to one of my friends that I quietly slipped it into his hands. It is not, however, lost to me, for I can always hear its hollow reverberations when I visit it in its new abode.

From Berkeley we went to Leland Stanford University and the Hopkins seaside laboratory of this institution at Pacific Grove. Here we met the director of the laboratory, Dr. W. K. Fisher, several other biological associates, and Miss Julia Platt, a former member of our Cambridge laboratory, who had settled in Pacific Grove and had in fact served the town as mayor. After many interesting experiences about Berkeley we bade adieu to our kind host and hostess there, Mr. and Mrs. H. F. Jackson, and traveled by train to Los Angeles. Here we visited La Brea asphalt pits, deposits of semi-liquid tar, the glistening surface of which as it spread out over the land looks so much like that of water as to entice unwary, thirsty animals into its fatal trap where, like flies, they meet with their final destruction. We watched the workmen in the pits laboriously exhuming the skeletons of prehistoric creatures, such as that of the saber-toothed tiger; the collection of these skeletons in the local county museum is the finest in the world. We were on our way to the Scripp's Oceanographic Institute at La Jolla near San Diego and were so limited in time that we could not then visit the county museum. At a subsequent visit to the laboratory at La Jolla we did attempt the museum, but under rather strange circumstances. We had postponed our visit to the collection of tiger skeletons till we were on our way east, when in passing through Los Angeles we were to have ample time between trains to see the exhibition. On arriving at the museum we found to our dismay that its doors were closed, though the weekday was one on which the museum might well have been open. Repeated applications to the bell at the side of the entrance finally brought a watchman, who informed us that the day was a California holiday and hence the museum was shut. He further added, as though we should know the fact, that it was Admission Day in the state. This seemed to me under the circumstances a strange designation till the watchman informed us that the day was in celebration of the admission of California into the Union. After some parley, in which he came to learn my situation, he told us that if we would go to a freight entrance at the rear of the building and would wait there a short time he would admit us privately and we could view the collection. This we did, and thus we enjoyed a quiet and full inspection of this wonderful exhibition of most remarkable animal skeletons. Having accomplished our object, we thanked the watchman, and made our exit at the private rear entrance of the establishment.

But before I proceed eastward I must say a word or so about the Oceanographic Laboratory at La Jolla where we had been staying. This laboratory was established through the efforts of my old friend and associate of Harvard graduate days, Dr. William E. Ritter, and by funds contributed by Miss Ellen Scripps and her brother, Mr. Edward W. Scripps, of newspaper fame. The Scripps family did much for La Jolla, but nothing so considerable as the founding of its celebrated marine laboratory. Situated some fifteen miles from San Diego and two miles north of its suburb, La Jolla, the laboratory enjoys a superb position on the Pacific front. This is at once independent of the towns and yet near enough to them to have all the urban conveniences. My few days' visit at the Scripps Laboratory showed me that the opportunities for work there, both in equipment and in the marine animals available, made it a most desirable location for biological investigations and I resolved, therefore, to arrange if possible for an early and lengthy visit at the place. As a matter of fact my wife and I spent two summer seasons at this laboratory, one in 1916, and the other in 1919. On the second of these, after I had settled down to my work in a comfortable laboratory room, I was interrupted in my affairs by the sudden entrance into my quarters of Mr. Scripps with the direct question, "Who are you?" I told him, whereupon he asked further, "What brings you here? You are the first outsider who has come to this place for a second time." I then remarked as information to Mr. Scripps that Mrs. Parker took great pleasure in being at La Jolla, and that when we were here she cooked for me and that I enjoyed food prepared by her better than I did that prepared by any other person. Hence, to come to the laboratory was a very pleasant experience for us both. He then wished to know where Mrs. Parker was and when I told him in which bungalow we were living, he went there in his car, and carried her off for a long ride over southern California which nearly cost me my next meal. Thus began a rough and ready friendship with "E. W.," as Mr. Scripps was commonly called, that added greatly to the pleasure of our La Jolla sojourn. I shall defer an account of my work at La Jolla till I take up in detail my zoological doings.

But to return to our first visit to California. We concluded this all too short and hasty tour of this land of marvels by leaving San Diego for the east in late September, 1914. Our railroad tickets called for a day's stopover at the Grand Canyon. We felt much surfeited with sight-seeing and we doubted if, after all our experiences, even the widely advertised Grand Canyon would mean much to us. We arrived at the canyon station by train early in the morning and walked at once to the rim. Never before in my life has my breath been so taken from me by the vastness and grandeur of a view! To look down into this stupendous valley a mile deep and across its extent for some thirteen miles to the opposite rim went far beyond anything else we had seen in all our wanderings. We asked nothing more than to sit on the edge of the canyon and watch the ever-changing panorama as in a sunny sky the cloud-shadows drifted slowly from place to place and the illumination of the whole changed with the shifting of the light. The colors of the rocks, the endless detail of their sculpturing, and the glimpses here and there of the thread of river physically responsible for it, all was a sight that nothing which we had seen before could equal. At the end of the day we deserted this natural marvel with the feeling that without premeditation and wholly unintentionally we had left the greatest sight of all to the last. Our train sped us eastward and in what seemed to us an incredibly short time we found ourselves back in quiet, subdued Cambridge, where the only gold to be seen was that on the distant dome of the State House on Beacon Hill.

XIX

Japan

NIPPON, THE LAND OF THE RISING SUN
Century Dictionary and Cyclopedia

THE third Pan-Pacific Science Congress was arranged to meet in the autumn of 1926 at Tokyo, Japan. Harvard University was invited to send a delegate and President Lowell requested me to seek out someone among the biologists who would be willing to serve in this capacity. After a futile search I was forced to report to the President that no one seemed available, whereupon he remarked, "And why do not you go?" I replied that as I had been asked to find someone, I supposed that that excluded me from consideration. He declared to the contrary, and I told him that I would be very glad to take the matter up with Mrs. Parker, for the invitation included the wife or another lady in the delegate's family. My wife looked on the project with favor, and I so informed the President. The Harvard Corporation made a very generous provision for us in that it granted me an ample traveling fellowship and permission to adjust my college work so that I could be away from Cambridge from June 1926 till February 1927.

We planned to do as much sight-seeing as we reasonably could on our way to Tokyo and back. We left Cambridge in June 1926, visited Glacier National Park, and then at Vancouver took steamer for the inland passage to Alaska, a trip which carried us through some of the most superb mountain scenery of the northwest. From Skagway, where we left the steamer, we went by train to White Horse and the White Horse Rapids and then returned over much the same route to San Francisco. Here we embarked on a Dollar Line boat for the Hawaiian Islands where we remained about a month, mostly in Honolulu. From Honolulu and its interesting Waikiki Beach, the Pali, and the like, we made a trip of a week or so to the Island of Hawaii proper to visit the celebrated volcano of Kilauea.

This unfortunately was inactive at the time, but at the volcano laboratory we had the pleasure of renewing our acquaintance with the director, Dr. Thomas A. Jagger, whom we had known at Harvard; he showed us almost everything of special interest in the neighborhood of the volcano.

We traveled about the island in an automobile with a native Hawaiian, John Acuni by name, as chauffeur. John was a veritable mine of the traditions of the island. As we were driving along a partly shaded road one of our party reached out and pulled a small branch from a flowering tree. John immediately told us that the tree was a rain tree and that breaking off a branch would surely bring on a shower of rain. We asked if nothing could be done to prevent the threatened calamity. John thought a moment and then told us that if we put three stones in a pile, one on the other, then drove away watching the stones, and if the pile remained intact till it was out of sight, the rain would be prevented. We tried the charm and it worked to perfection. John, perceiving that we were sympathetic to his views, now began to talk freely with us. We had come to a spot where a half year or so before a lava flow had crossed the road and John pointed out to us its peculiar course, for it had avoided one farm in the lower country and had buried another. Finally it had entered the sea. Where it had crossed the road it was still very hot, hot enough to set fire to a stick thrust into a crack in it and yet not so hot that it could not be driven over rapidly. John then told us that before the flow had occurred a strange woman had been seen on the road. She begged a ride of a Chinaman who was driving to his farm, but was refused by the oriental. Another Chinese farmer coming later gave her a lift. She then was seen down near the sea where she begged a fish from some fishermen who had a large stock of live fish in an artificial sea pool where they held the fish for a good market. They, like the first farmer, denied her request and told her the fish did not belong to them, but to their masters in Hilo. Then she disappeared, and soon after that the lava began to flow from an opening in the side of the volcano. The stream passed down the incline, crossed the road where we had seen it, and passed by the farm of the man who had given the woman a ride, destroyed that of the one who had denied her help, and poured into the fish pools where her request had also been denied, ruining them and killing all the fish. After this detailed account John said:

"That woman was Madam Pele, the goddess of the volcano." He added, "Mr. Parker, we do not talk this way in town [meaning Hilo], but we talk so out here in the country among ourselves, and all that I tell you is true, really true, for we Hawaiians know it." This was only a beginning of John's many tales, but before we said goodbye to him we came to realize what an astoundingly superstitious race the Hawaiians were. With this foretaste of eastern mentality we left the Hawaiian Islands for a two weeks' passage to Japan.

We reached the port of Kobe, Japan, about the middle of September 1926, and just after the last typhoon for that season had blown itself out. Japan is generally known as the Land of the Rising Sun, and geographically this is most appropriate, for it is on the eastern edge of Asia. But we can describe a nation in other ways than global terms. Italy has always been to me the land of great external beauty, France the region of finest perceptions, and England the home of wholesome truthfulness. From such standpoints I would call Japan the country of the greatest politeness. In no region in all my travels have I met with a national politeness equal to that of Japan. Even if driven to an extreme a Japanese remains essentially polite. He will endeavor in every way he can not to be rude or discourteous, and always to do or say that which is agreeable or acceptable to his neighbor. And he will do this at the expense of truth. Most occidentals estimate truth so highly that they will maintain it even to the point of extreme rudeness, but not so the inhabitants of Japan. They will strain the truth rather than say something that may give offense. We occidentals are prone to look down on this as a defect, but the Japanese may react in the same way to our worship of truth. Some partly westernized inhabitants of Japan have come to accept our view in this matter, but in so doing they have made themselves less acceptable to their countrymen.

When we arrived in Tokyo for the coming congress we were met at the railroad station by a group of Japanese gentlemen who welcomed us to the city and who escorted us to the Imperial Hotel where we were to stay. After this attention they dropped away one by one till only a single member of the group was left. He was an old university associate of mine whom I had known well in America where we were students together in the Harvard laboratories. As I walked with him to the door of the hotel at the conclusion of his call he took me by the arm and said, "Parker, it is with us here and now as it was in America long ago. I shall always tell you the truth and I can assure you that few other Japanese will do so. Whenever you want to know what the facts are, ask me." And I found that all the information which I got from him subsequently was in every way reliable. Not that the others lied to us, but they almost invariably strained the truth to be agreeable. In my opinion a profound sense of politeness rather than one of truthfulness is a basic feature in the Japanese character, and though it is often construed to the disadvantage of this eastern people it may not be so construed with full justice to them.

As I have said, we left the ship at Kobe in September 1926, but when we were two days from this port, and before we had seen land, we received a wireless message from some of our Japanese friends welcoming us to their shore. We arrived at Kobe in a pouring rain. There, at the outer end of the wharf under an umbrella in all the downpour, was my former student, Dr. T. Kawamura from Kyoto, ready to greet us. He passed us and our luggage at once through the customs, for he told us that as delegates to the congress we were exempt from such restrictions, and escorted us to the Kyoto train. Together we rode to his home town. On the way he gave me, with the compliments of the Japanese government, a railroad pass for the use of my wife and myself for as long as we were in the islands. Such reception and treatment nearly took my breath away, but it was only the beginning. Kawamura conducted us to an excellent hotel in Kyoto, the Miyako, where we were given a beautiful room, the end of which folded back fully, disclosing a delightful view over the city. After our first night there, during which we slept with our room freely open to the outer air, I was awakened by the roaring of something strangely like a lion. I went to the open end of our apartment only to discover that we were well above the zoological garden of Kyoto and actually in the neighborhood of the lion cages. When, that morning, I told Kawamura what had wakened me and taxed him with this unusual zoological touch, he laughed but maintained that the lion chorus was a pure accident in which he had had no part. Thus began our acquaintance with this nation under the Sun Goddess, the wonders of which grew upon us as time went on.

By a mere coincidence I happened to have intimate Japanese

friends at each of the four important universities. At Kyoto, the ancient capital of Japan, near the head of the inland sea and in the region where the Sun Goddess was supposed to have entered the islands, was Dr. T. Kawamura, already spoken of. I first met Dr. Kawamura when, a casual visitor as I supposed, he came one autumn to Harvard. I conducted him over the laboratories, the zoological library, and the Agassiz Museum, and then in the evening I took him to a dinner of the Academy Round Table in Boston and after that to a meeting of the American Academy of Arts and Sciences. He seemed pleased at what he saw and impressed by the number of scientific men in our community. After the meeting of the Academy I bade him adieu at his hotel, supposing that he was to continue his travels; but I was surprised to have him request another interview with me the next day. I agreed to meet him at our laboratory and when he came he expressed a wish to work under me for the coming winter. I assured him that I should be very glad to receive him as a student, whereupon he remarked with a twinkle in his eye, "Now you are my professor and I may not come nearer than seven feet from you or I might step on your shadow which would be very improper." We both laughed at this half serious pleasantry, but I began there and then to sense the possibilities of Japanese etiquette. Thus commenced my friendship with Dr. Kawamura and it was through advice from him that in coming to Japan we landed at Kobe, the port nearest Kyoto. At Kyoto we also found other old friends, Dr. and Mrs. Komai, both of whom I had become well acquainted with at Woods Hole in former years. They, with the Kawamuras, did much to make our introduction to Japan easy and pleasant. At Tokyo, as head of the zoological laboratory, was Dr. S. Goto, a student associate of mine in the early days of the Harvard laboratory, and at Sendai in the north was Dr. Ekitaro Nomura who had been a student under me at the Cambridge Laboratory. In the extreme north, at Sapporo in the Hokkaido, was Dr. K. Miyabe, an old and intimate friend who had worked under Dr. Farlow at the Harvard cryptogamic laboratory.

Through these former Japanese associates it was arranged that I should lecture at several of their university centers. At Kyoto University I gave a conference on the evolution of mind, and later I was taken by Dr. Kawamura to Osaka where in Asahi Hall, the largest auditorium in which I believe I ever spoke, I lectured on the seals of the Pribilof Islands. The lecture was given under the auspices of the principal Japanese newspaper of that city. It was illustrated by lantern slides and was delivered in a remarkable way. I talked in very direct and simple English for three or four minutes and then Dr. Kawamura, who was with me on the platform, translated my remarks into Japanese. Thus, step by step, we covered the subject of the lecture in the course of about an hour and a half. After the lecture was over I expressed my surprise to Dr. Kawamura that such a subject should attract so large an audience, for there were literally thousands of listeners in the huge auditorium. He told me that such audiences flocked to public lectures of this kind chiefly to acquaint themselves with spoken English, and that I must not feel too much flattered either about myself or my subject. At Tokyo Dr. Goto arranged for me to give four academic lectures on the organization of the nervous system. These were well attended and it was a great pleasure for me to greet in my audience Dr. Sho Watase, an old companion of early Woods Hole days.

Mrs. Parker and I both went to Sendai to visit the university there and for the lecture I was to give. Several days before we were to leave Tokyo for Sendai Dr. Nomura of that university called on us at our hotel in Tokyo and told us that he had been sent to escort us north. We protested and explained that we were not yet ready to go, but he waved our objections aside and insisted that he would gladly await our pleasure. In fact he suggested that that evening we go out with him as his guests to a restaurant which he had in mind and to which he wished very much to take us. He had us driven through Tokyo in the direction of Uyeno Park, and finally to a restaurant where we occupied a private room looking over a most beautiful stretch of level country and water. Here we had a delicious Japanese repast and were entertained by one of the singing girls who sat with us. Our room was separated from the adjacent rooms by the usual Japanese paper sliding partitions through which the voices of our neighbors could be easily heard. Nomura assured himself by question that we did not understand the neighboring conversation, for said he, "What they say in the adjacent rooms is not for your ears." After an evening which to us was in all respects interesting and enjoyable, we left the restaurant by stepping over the door sill with its three purifying miniature pyramids of salt, the sign of this class of restaurants, and motored back to the hotel. As Nomura bade us good night, he remarked, "You have for some time been looking at the top layers of Tokyo. Now you have seen its bottom." We all three laughed and he went away.

He met us at the Uyeno station, Tokyo, at an appointed time a day or so later and we took the afternoon train for Sendai. My wife had devised a game that she played with the names of the railway stations in Japan and which taught her much Japanese. Each principal station had on a signboard its name in Japanese characters and in English letters. Next to it, on the same board, was the name in Japanese of the last station passed and of the next to come and, while the train was moving toward that station, my wife with her pocket dictionary would try to work out in English the name of the station we were approaching. At that station she could get the answer to her problem, for there the name would be in English as well as in Japanese. In this way she taught herself many Japanese characters, much to the amusement of Dr. Nomura. I asked him what I, without knowledge of Japanese, could learn from the conductor on the train about the next station, and he advised me to try. When the conductor again came through our car I beckoned to him and asked him in English the name of the next station. He bowed his head sheepishly, indicating that he did not understand, but produced from his pocket a pad of paper and a pencil and indicated that I should write out my query. This I did in English, to which he in turn wrote the answer, also in English. Spoken English could not be understood by him, but written English he had mastered.

When we were about an hour from Sendai, Nomura told me that all the university professors in zoology and botany, with their wives and children, some fifty persons in all, would be there to welcome us and that it would be necessary for me to speak to them in Japanese. This I protested I could not do, but he insisted that I should learn a short speech in the tongue of the land; and he proceeded to give me my lesson. After some practice I mastered in a rude way a single Japanese sentence. When in the early evening we reached Sendai, there, sure enough, was a large congregation of Japanese, all in their best attire to greet us. We all bowed in Japanese fashion—bent at our middles with our heads projected forward. Nomura was directly behind me and as I began to return to the upright position, he punched me from behind and said, "Say your speech."

Whereupon, as I arose I said, "Minasan komban wa omukai arigato gozaimasu," which means, roughly translated, "Ladies and Gentlemen, thank you for this evening's reception." With much applause we were thus introduced. After these simple formalities had passed off, we were escorted to the Sendai hotel and put up in its one western room, the inside of the door of which had painted upon it in most delicate tints a very beautiful picture of a crouching tiger. Here we lived for our brief stay in Sendai. Nomura called at the hotel for us each morning with a program for the day and gave word to those in the hotel what our needs would be, for no one there understood English.

The Sendai hotel was strictly Japanese, and as soon as we were settled there I told my wife that we should be expected to take the usual late afternoon Japanese bath. I went below, found a hotel functionary, and indicated by motions that we both wished to bathe and that we would await in our room upstairs a call to the bath. After a quarter of an hour or so a diminutive Japanese servant with little more than a loincloth on, and with an array of towels in his arms, came to our door and we each, covered with only a kimono, were shown by him to the bathroom. This was a room some fifteen feet square with a sloping, wooden floor and a sunken wooden tank of warm water at one end. The walls of the room were wood except at their tops which were glazed. I knew it was the duty of the servant to stay with us till we had washed with soap and then to scrub our backs, but my wife would not remove her kimono, her only covering, with the boy present and I had great difficulty in making him understand that we did not need his service further and that we would attend to each other's backs. Finally he departed, with seeming reluctance. We then slipped off our single coverings, and like Adam and Eve in the garden, we began the bath. We sat upon low wooden stools, dipped a hand-tub of water out of the large tank of warm water and poured it over our bodies. Then we scrubbed ourselves thoroughly with soap and water till we were completely clean, the soapy water draining off from us down the inclined floor and out by an escape opening. After we had become quite clean and had rinsed all soapy water from our bodies by repeated applications of clear water, we went through the purely social stage of the function. This consisted in entering the large tank of warm water and immersing ourselves up to our necks there. Thus immersed, we remained some length of time, talking small talk as you would at an afternoon tea, and then having become completely warmed through and through, which to a Japanese in cold weather is a great comfort, we climbed out of the tank, dried ourselves with towels, put on our kimonos, and the ceremony of the bath was at an end. We then walked to our hotel room. I had endeavored to carry out the whole affair with as much privacy as I could, though I knew that to a Japanese a general exposure of the person was in no sense improper. Still, out of deference to my wife and our western habits, I steered our bathing as near as I could toward our western ways. That the bath was far from private we both learned on emerging from the bathroom when we discovered that most of the personnel of the hotel, some score or more of persons, had assembled in the hall surrounding the bathroom and were peering in through its upper glazed wall to see how Americans took a Japanese bath. They acted as though there was nothing improper in this freedom, for they kindly made way for us as we passed by. These Sendaians were interested in us merely as foreign objects who had been injected into their native environment. In Japan the general exposure of the naked body to the view of others is not, as it is with us, an impropriety. It was interesting to see, at some of the hot spring bathing resorts, men, women, and children quite without clothing, but with small towels held modestly before them, walk up to the spouting, warm water, bathe and then retire, the whole affair taking place on a roadside along which an indifferent public passed. This freedom from an abnormal curiosity about the uncovered bodies of others, which recalls certain aspects of the life of ancient Greece, has much to be said for it and may be an example which occidentals might do well to ponder.

Soon after we had arrived in Japan, and while we were still in Kyoto, Dr. and Mrs. Komai took us on an excursion to Ise. This is the chief Shinto shrine in Japan and the abode of the Sun Goddess. Such revered objects as the mirror and the crystal ball are said to be here. We were surprised to learn that the Komais had never before visited Ise; although they were Christians they said that out of reverence to their ancestors they did not hesitate to worship at Ise. Its shrine, every board of which was faultless and perfect, was a simple wooden structure located in a beautiful grove of cryptomeria trees. The paths leading to the shrine were immaculately clean and orderly and the surrounding shrubbery was in the best of form. The little river by which we passed had a stony shore, every pebble of which seemed clean and in place. Even the fish in the stream were quiet and composed. The whole region was one of refined and simple dignity. We too entered into its spirit. Here anyone might repose in quiet reflection and ponder what he owes to those who went before. We left the shrine with a sense of sincere gratefulness.

The late afternoon railroad connections for our departure from Ise were not favorable and we spent the ensuing night at the Gonikwai Hotel in the neighboring town of Yamada. Here we were ushered past beautiful Japanese rooms to the one European apartment in the hotel where we found an odd mixture of western furniture. We intimated to the Komais that we should much prefer to live in Japanese fashion and were immediately transferred into one of the delightful Japanese apartments with an outlook over a beautiful garden. Here the Komais conducted us through the full range of Japanese life in a hotel. We bathed in Japanese fashion, had our meal on cushions on the floor, and were eventually put to bed at that level. After the *naisan* who had attended to us had made up our beds upon the floor I called her attention to my length and to the length of my bed. She did not at first understand me, but after I had stretched out on my couch and she saw that my head protruded far beyond the limits of the bed at one end and my feet at the other she laughed heartily, ran away and soon returned with a second body of bedding in her arms and added it to one end of what she had already arranged. Thus on a doubly extended bed I rested well for the night. The next day we left Yamada, visited Nagoya with its palace pinnacled with golden whales, Gifu with its picturesque cormorant fishing by torchlight and so on to Tokyo, the congress, and our departure.

The meetings of the Pan-Pacific Science Congress were modeled on those of other such world assemblies. The congress was under the patronage of His Imperial Highness Prince Kotohito and under the presidency of Dr. J. Sakurai of Tokyo Imperial University. There were general meetings and special sectional meetings which gave opportunity for a flood of scientific papers of all kinds and from many sources. The course of the meetings was punctuated by business assemblies, by outdoor entertainments, and by luncheons, dinners, and numerous other social functions. Most interesting, perhaps, were the special excursions to significant parts of Japan, to the temples at Nikko, to the lake region around Fujiyama, to Kamakura and Enoshima and other like places. One of the most distant of these excursions was to the Hokkaido in the north with a visit to an Ainu village. The present Ainu are the remnants of a primitive race that peopled the islands before the Japanese came. They are a counterpart of our American Indians, but unlike the latter they seem to be dying out. We were conducted through some of their villages by Dr. John Batchelor, an English missionary who had spent most of his life amongst them. He had learned their language, written a grammar and a dictionary of it and was thoroughly conversant with their traditions. He persuaded the chief at one of the villages to offer up a prayer to the Ainu gods in the Ainu language, and in our presence it was very sincerely and reverently done. I asked Dr. Batchelor what the chief said and he told me that he called on the gods, told them that strangers were in his house, and asked them to understand that he was complying to the request of these strangers by addressing a few words to them. He then concluded by making a libation to the gods, imploring them not to be offended at his act. Dr. Batchelor told us of the great consideration that the Ainu always showed him as he circulated amongst them, for it was his custom from time to time to carry to them official information that might be issued for their guidance by the Japanese government. At each village the chief would entertain him and the chief's wife would prepare for him a special meal. On one occasion the woman of the house placed before him an unusual dish in the form of a prepared bird. He complimented her on the delicacy of what he supposed to be a woodcock, to which she replied, "Oh, sir, it is not a woodcock. It is a chicken." As chicken is a great rarity with these people, Dr. Batchelor replied, "What, you have killed a chicken for me?" "No, sir," said his hostess, "it died yesterday." Dr. Batchelor said he found that he must be prepared for any kind of emergency. The wife of another chief, whose kitchen was noted for a special kind of cookie, offered him a fresh baking of her delicacies, served in a covered piece of imported English crockery which as a particular honor for him she had gone to town and bought. Dr. Batchelor said he had not the heart to tell the kind soul that the piece of crockery which she had chosen was kept, when in use, under the beds of western people. Thus we had a glimpse into the simple, kindly life of this vanishing race.

The impressions that we carried away with us from Japan, as given in the present chapter, were those of a most friendly and generous people, courteous and considerate to the last degree. But how profoundly all this has been changed by the happenings of the last decade! It would seem that the nation of greatest politeness had come to be a nation of shocking treachery and intense brutality. It is true that the nation with the greatest politeness which we saw was a nation as a whole at home and in peace, and that the nation of brutality was that nation's army in foreign wars. But the change means something more than this. It shows, I believe, that politeness of itself is not a cardinal virtue. To be of real social value, politeness must be subordinate to a respect for truth which not infrequently must override the minor virtue. A rugged truthfulness scarcely ever finds its place in Japanese conduct, and a polite rejoinder, as given by a Japanese, may often carry with it a note of unintentional insincerity. This, in my opinion, is a common weakness in the character of many Japanese. Often when I was talking over matters with some of my acquaintances in this oriental empire I wished for my old companion of college days, that I might know from him the real truth of what was being said. But however this may be, and to what extent we may attribute such acts as those of Pearl Harbor and the like to a treachery and insincerity in the Japanese, I am convinced that the outburst of the last ten years in Japan which has led that nation into a disastrous war and an ignominious defeat rests upon much deeper biological difficulties than those associated with an overruling politeness and its consequences, all of which in my opinion are relatively superficial matters. These underlying biological troubles of a nation such as Japan I shall take up at the close of the next chapter.

XX

China

IN THE COUNTRY OF KATHAY

Marco Polo

WE left Japan proper at Shimonoseki on the twentieth of November, 1926, and took the so-called Tsushima ferry boat for Fusan, Korea, on the mainland of Asia. Here we arrived early in the morning of the next day, and then went by train to Seoul, the capital of Korea. The Korean countryside is singularly destitute of trees, for the Koreans had used their forests without replanting. We were told, in fact, that they were reduced to digging up tree stumps and roots for firewood. Some of the villages at this time of year had great piles of bundled weeds which were their only possible household preparation for the rigor of a cold winter. The Koreans are an unusually tall people. Out of respect to their recently deceased emperor they all wore white clothes and top hats, the Korean sign of mourning, and these tall white figures with their strange headdresses as they stalked across the land, for walking seemed to be their common method of locomotion, made a strange picture viewed from the train. In Seoul we visited the Chosen Christian College, Serverance Hospital, and the Korean Palace, a beautiful building more or less hidden by a modern public structure built in front of it by the Japanese who we soon found were far from loved by the Koreans.

From Seoul we went by train to Mukden in Manchuria. Here the Japanese railroad ends and the Chinese line begins and here order and security seemed to cease and a mild chaos to take its place, for we were now arriving in the country of Chang Tso-lin, the land of banditry. At Mukden Dr. I. Ohga, professor of botany at the Educational Institute, took us in the late afternoon to a remarkable tomb of a Chinese emperor, now much fallen into decay. It was a large brick and stone structure of imposing architecture, more or less buried by the sands of the surrounding hills. As we walked about it we met a group of Chinese students who wished to obtain some information from us on matters American, and did so by a most remarkable system of linguistic circumlocution. The students could read and write Chinese but nothing else. Dr. Ohga could read and write Japanese and speak English but not Chinese. My wife and I were limited to English. The salvation of the situation was the fact that the written characters in Chinese and in Japanese are about the same, though the spoken languages are entirely unlike. In this respect the Chinese and Japanese characters are like our European Arabic figures. In our oriental chain of communication the Chinese students wrote out their questions, directed to my wife and me, in Chinese, the characters of which could be read and understood by Dr. Ohga who then communicated the question to us in English. Our answer then went back on the same linguistic chain but in reverse order. Thus, partly by spoken and partly by written signs we could, through our Japanese intermediary, converse with the Chinese. They too were interested visitors at the Chinese tomb and gathered some information about it from Dr. Ohga.

In Mukden we stayed overnight at the railroad hotel which seemed to be a center of a small riot in the railroad square during most of the night. In the morning I was told by the Chinese officials that that day's train to Peking, which would make the trip in a little over twenty-four hours, was fully sold out and that we must wait over a day or more there for places on a later train. I then consulted with the Japanese railroad officials. They confirmed the statements of the Chinese, but advised me to settle my hotel bill, pack my luggage and be ready to take the train, for places were sometimes given up on the train at the last moment and those on hand would be substituted for the absentees. I did as advised and found, as the passengers were being put on the train, that a mistake had been made in the assignment of a compartment with two berths in it; one berth had been assigned to a man from New York and the other to a young woman from Cambridge, on the erroneous assumption that she was a man. As this compartment was being vacated our Japanese helper put our luggage in it, my wife and I followed, and the train soon moved off, leaving the New Yorker gesticulating on the railroad platform and literally swearing venge-

ance on the Chinese officials for their mistake. The displaced young
woman remained on the train and was paired off with another person of her own sex in a compartment in another part of the car.
Thus, by mere luck, we moved on at once to Peking. The contrast
of this Chinese train with the Japanese one that brought us to
Mukden was most pronounced. The Chinese train was made up of
a few ramshackle, worn-out cars occupied mostly by a body of
Chang Tso-lin's soldiers who, I afterwards learned, were to be
our protective guard against bandits as far as Peking. They spent
most of their time sleeping on the tables of a section of one car
used as a diner. Here I got such food as we ate and carried it into
our compartment rather than have my wife eat from a table half of
which might be occupied by sleeping Chinese guards. In the evening we reached Shanaikwan where the Great Wall of China
touches the sea, and here we passed out of Manchuria and into
real China. We arrived at Peking a little before noon on the next
day. At the railroad station just outside the city walls we were
met by American friends, Dr. Bertram Read of the Peking Union
Medical College, and Dr. N. Gist Gee of the Rockefeller Foundation, whose family name though suggestive of Chinese is that of an
American from our own southern states. These two gentlemen took
us to the Wagons-Lits Hotel in the foreign quarter of the city
and next to the compound of the United States legation. It was a
pleasure to see, daily floating overhead and not far from us, the
Stars and Stripes. At the Wagons-Lits we found excellent accommodations which served us as such during our stay in Peking.

Our two weeks in this remarkable capital were weeks of novel
and pleasurable experiences. On the day of our arrival we were
taken to the Club of the Western Returned Students for a Thanksgiving dinner. Here we met Dr. Wong of the Geological Survey
and Dr. S. King, at whose beautiful house we were subsequently
entertained; the repast on this occasion included birds-nest soup,
Peking duck, ancient jellied eggs, and other luxuries known to us
heretofore only by name. At a dinner at Dr. Gee's we met Dr.
DeVries, son of the Dutch botanist, whom I had known abroad,
and my old friend Dr. Fortuyn, also a Dutchman. We were
taken to luncheons and dinners almost beyond numbers, to
Dr. George Barbour's where we met Mrs. Barbour, an old family
friend, to Dr. Davidson Black's, to Dr. La Force's and to Dr.

Faust's. We drove out to Yengching University where I had been asked to lecture. Here we met President Stuart and here too we were entertained most delightfully at luncheon by Miss Alice Boring of the department of zoology. At Tsing Hua University, the Indemnity College, we were dined in full Chinese fashion. Fortunately we were now proficient in the use of chopsticks. I gave lectures before both the Peking Natural History Society and the Peking Union Medical College. The latter institution in its Chinese garb was a most interesting place. In appearance Chinese, its spirit was western. Dr. Robert Lim's physiological laboratory, both in equipment and in work, might well have been in any western university center. We were told that the ordinary Chinese were only gradually induced to try western medicine and that few came for such treatment without being at the same time under a Chinese physician. The progress of western medicine in China has much to overcome and the experiment of the so-called P.U.M.C. still hangs in the balance. The recent Japanese invasion has done the movement great harm, and it cannot yet be surmised what the outcome will be. At the time of our visit only Chang Tso-lin's soldiers were in the city and, as our kindly reception and entertainment shows, they were not a serious menace.

From Peking we took only one extended outside excursion. This was an automobile trip to the Great Wall and the Ming Tombs. We left Peking early one morning by car and made our way to Nankow where we boarded a small train to Nankow Pass. The train consisted regularly of an open car and a boxcar without seats for the short run to the pass. The day we made the tour was a most beautifully clear winter day with a sharp northwest wind. It would have been very exposing for us in the last part of our run in the boxcar, but fortunately on that day an excursion of American tourists was being conducted from Tientsin to the wall and several steam heated cars were added to the train. This train stopped at Nankow and rather surreptitiously we slipped into one of the heated cars and thus got a warm ride to the pass. Here we left the train, climbed the short incline, and gained the Great Wall at one of its gates. It was bitter cold in the strong winter wind, but I literally dragged my wife up the passageway and out on the wall and together we looked over the wintery plain to distant Kulgan. Mrs. Parker then retreated to a warmer situation while I walked out a quarter of a mile or so along the roadway on the top of the wall. The Wall was visible for many miles as it wound over the hills in both directions. It looked like nothing so much as a gigantic serpent stretching over hill and valley for many miles. We were told that it had been built by a Chinese emperor about the beginning of the Christian Era to keep intruders out of China, but that it had failed entirely in its purpose and had resulted only in keeping the Chinese in. We were glad to return to the train and its warmth. After having thawed myself out in the cars I again went out and walked about in the neighborhood of the railroad station, for we still had an hour or so before leaving. To one side I found a low stone and brick hovel out of a small door of which there came a little Chinese boy done up in his winter, padded clothes. He had a friendly face and beckoned me to come to a still smaller structure built on the side of the hovel. Through the roof of this diminutive hut he extracted a small very clean piglet, evidently his pet. He held it out to me and I stroked it, greatly to his delight. He then put the piglet, which seemed to be very well cared for, into its small pen and indicated to me that I should stay where I was. Thereupon he disappeared into the main hut, but quickly returned with a very small camel bell on a string. This he presented to me as a token of our new friendship and then disappeared into the hut, apparently overcome by his boldness. Nor did I see him again. This childish present I still have with me and I cherish it, I believe, more fully than I do any other article that I brought with me from China.

From the Great Wall we went to Nankow by train and then by automobile to the Tangshan Hot-spring Hotel. Here, heated by the hot water that bubbles up from the earth, we remained overnight to motor the next day to the Ming Tombs. We passed up the great entrance avenue of gigantic animals—elephants, camels and the like, one standing on its feet and the next kneeling—till we reached in the midst of the mountains the group of perhaps a dozen great tombs of the Ming emperors. After climbing over one or two of these gigantic structures we returned to our automobile, motored to the Jade Fountain with its wonderful flow of water, the Sleeping Buddha, the Temple of the Great Bell, and so back to the Wagons-Lits in Peking. These are a few of the many things that we did in and about this strangely dream-like city.

The city of the Manchus, the Forbidden City within the Walls, the immense Chinese City, the Temple of Agriculture and the Altar of Heaven beyond the Walls—to view Peking as a whole is impossible. To walk on the city walls and look over the vast expanse of museums, palaces, and temples with their gracefully curved tile roofs, their garden enclosures, all in soft yellows, reds, and greens and with the western hills in the far background is to see a picture never to be forgotten. The summer after my return to the United States I met at Woods Hole Mr. Charles R. Crane who remarked that he had not seen me there as usual and I replied that I had been traveling in the Far East. He then said, "And did you see Peking?" to which he added, on hearing that my wife and I had spent some two weeks there, "You have seen the one great capital of the world," a profoundly true statement.

December 1926 was a critical war period in North China. We were continually told that perhaps the last train had left Peking. Finally on the afternoon of December eighth we awaited the afternoon train for our trip to Tientsin. The train came in several hours late and as its passengers left it we and many others entered. We sat there several hours while the engine was being refueled and shifted to the other end of the train. But even when all seemed ready and the train was heavily loaded nothing happened. No one dared to leave, for a place lost might not be recovered. Finally in the evening we began to move toward Tientsin. When about half the distance to our destination had been covered we came to a standstill out in the open country. On inquiry it appeared that one of Chang Tso-lin's wives was on her way to Peking and that our engine was needed to move her train there. This it did, and after several hours' delay it returned to us and carried us slowly to Tientsin. We arrived about midnight and our whole train emptied out. My wife and I with our luggage gained the station platform with what seemed to be a thousand jabbering, gesticulating Chinese. What to do was the question! Here we were at the railroad station of a dark, unknown town with no knowledge of the language or the place and among a hoard of milling strangers. I counseled remaining still in all the confusion. After a short time to my utmost surprise I heard a voice above the tumult shouting, "Dr. Parker, Dr. Parker." Never had I heard more welcome words. Presently a person made his way to us, explained that he was the agent of

Cook and Son, whose tickets we had bought, and was there to care for us. What a relief! He transported us to the Astor House Hotel and after seeing that we were provided with excellent accommodations for the night told us that he would call for us the next morning. After a night of real rest we were told by the Cook agent that the boat on which we had been assigned a passage for Shanghai was already filled and that we would be obliged to wait over a day in Tientsin for another vessel, but that we could count upon leaving for Shanghai the following day. Early that morning we went aboard the *Tongchow* and steaming down the Taku River crossed the bar about seven in the evening.

Our sea trip to Shanghai took some four days. On the way we called at Foochow where we saw on the wharf baskets of pongee silk cocoons, each cocoon as big as a pigeon's egg. Again at sea we passed fleets of Chinese fishing boats with gigantic guiding eyes painted on their bows. As we approached the mouth of the Yangtze Kiang I noted that the captain was uneasy. Finally we saw off to the right the stacks of a submerged steamer and we then learned that it was the boat of the day before on which we had failed to get passage. This boat in the fog had struck on the Amherst Rocks. All Europeans were saved, but without their luggage. Many Chinese were lost because they refused to leave their possessions when they were ordered to the lifeboats. This was the nearest we ever came to shipwreck. We were happy to land that evening on the Bund in Shanghai where we found good accommodations at the Palace Hotel.

The next morning while we were at breakfast we had a call from President Nance of Suchau University. He came to invite us for a day or two at Suchau. We knew that the war had reached such a stage that the railroad between Shanghai and Suchau could be cut at any time. However, President Nance assured us that if this occurred while we were in Suchau he could at any time transport us down Suchau Creek by motor boat under the protection of the international flag to Shanghai. We then arranged to go by train to Suchau and we were finally very glad that we did go, for Suchau proved to be the only unadulterated Chinese city which we visited. It is a walled town, square in outline some two miles to a side and with a population of about a million souls. Many of its streets are replaced by narrow canals, the water for which is led off from Suchau Creek. Hence it is often called the Venice of China. Its widest streets are so narrow that a rickshaw can move along them only with difficulty. No cars or carts enter the town. Its main street runs from one wall through the town to the opposite wall. At most places on the course of this thoroughfare you can touch the walls of opposite shops by extending your two arms. At one end of the main street is a temple and at the other a pagoda. These are said to anchor, one the head and the other the tail, of a dragon which, it is believed, lies buried under the street. No one may dig a well near the main street for fear of disturbing this tutelary beast. Cholera is said to be present in the town at most times and often seriously epidemic. The university is next to the city's wall in a compound of its own with some green stretches and a few trees. Here I lectured to an interesting audience of Chinese students, and here we stayed overnight. We visited shops of beautiful metal work, of curios, and of woven goods, silks and the like. The looms of Suchau were the chief sources of fabrics for the imperial court at Peking, and the inhabitants of Suchau were looking forward to a return of imperial rule in Peking so that they might start again with their weaving. This, however, will probably never come. We said adieu to our kind entertainers, Dr. and Mrs. Nance, and to Suchau with the feeling that we had at last seen a place Chinese to its core, for Peking was Manchurian and the coast towns we had visited were in large part foreign settlements. We returned to Shanghai by train and without mishap.

One of the great events of our Shanghai visit was to attend a performance in the Chinese theater by Mei Lang Fan, the celebrated Chinese actor. Through our hotel we purchased tickets for his performance. On the appointed evening we went to the theater and found the floor divided into square compartments in which were grouped Chinese families or gatherings of friends who had brought food and drink with them and were enjoying life while the play went on. This was carried out by a company of costumed actors who, with very simple properties and no scenery in the western sense, recited their parts to a musical accompaniment from a small group of artists on the stage. All this was for the entertainment of the audience till Mei Lang Fan was ready to come on. Several times during the night, for it was nearing midnight, a hushed and subdued murmur ran over the audience on the suspicion that the great actor was about to appear. Finally Mei Lang Fan, in the part of an exquisite woman, glided onto the stage with a group of supporting players all beautifully attired in the most delicate and refined colors. Mei Lang Fan spoke, or rather half-sang his part in flutelike tones and with gestures and motions of the greatest gracefulness. The whole performance seemed like a succession of groups from the finest Chinese porcelains accompanied with indescribably delicate instrumental and vocal tones projected on a spellbound audience whose responsive applause was a strange sucking in of the breath. Thus we western intruders were admitted to the intense yet suppressed enthusiasms of the best Chinese histrionics. It is strange that so delicate and refined a performance found so poor a reception when Mei Lang Fan came to the United States. Probably like certain fine wines this oriental performance would not bear transportation.

On December twenty-first we sailed from Shanghai on the Dollar Line steamer, *President Lincoln,* for Hongkong. On shipboard we became acquainted with the Bishop of London who was to give the Christmas sermon at the Hongkong cathedral. As we were interested to hear him speak we attended the service. He preached on what constitutes a Christian, and warned his hearers that the oriental idea that a Christian was one who did not use alcohol or tobacco was not true. He remarked that he partook of both and he then described in simple terms what he believed to be the real Christian virtues. He was a man of great honesty and spiritual power.

We had quarters at the Hongkong Hotel after having been disappointed to find that there was no hotel on the Peak. We were much interested in the mixture of races, predominantly Chinese, in the town and its suburbs. We crossed the water to Kowloon, a part of the British concession and took a drive in the open country. On the barren hillsides of this district were many tall jars that looked like upright beehives. On inquiry our Chinese driver told us that they were funeral urns and that each one contained the remains of a Chinese. I climbed up to one, looked into it, and there sure enough were the skull and bones of a human being with a parchment tag tied to the jar and inscribed in Chinese characters. The whole hillside was, we saw, a veritable mausoleum.

In wandering about Queen Street in Hongkong I noticed a Chi-

nese shop filled with interesting earthenware jars similar to some
my wife had given her in California for flowers. We were told at
that time that such jars were the containers of a very strong Chinese
drink. Here, then, in Hongkong was a real source of this article.
I entered the shop proposing to buy one, partly for my wife's collection and partly to taste the liquid, but the proprietor of the shop,
a Chinese, refused to sell me one and explained that he would get
into difficulties with the police if he sold his wares to any but
Chinese. I then persuaded a Chinese friend of mine to make the
purchase. This he did and thus I became the owner of a jar with
its original contents. The liquor, a transparent fluid of light color
and vicious alcoholic contents, was tasted by me and then, my
curiosity having been satisfied, discarded. The empty jar was
brought back by us as a souvenir. I was glad that this whole transaction did not bring me into the hands of the Hongkong police,
very tall East Indians who keep order on the street by openly shak-
ing and flogging disorderly persons as they see fit. The southern
Chinese, unlike their northern brothers, are small in person and in
the hands of an East Indian policeman they are like a mouse caught
by a cat. Nor does the Chinese resist his treatment.

One of our Hongkong days was given over to a steamboat ride
out to Macao and back. The name of this place had been familiar
to me from the days of my boyhood as a name on packages of
fourth of July firecrackers. The boat that carried us to Macao, the
Sui An, was a strange craft. Her pilothouse on the second deck was
well screened off with heavy wire netting as was her engine room
below, and her officers were well armed with heavy pistols. We
were told that the boat was from time to time taken by pirates
who infested the inland waters between Hongkong and Macao.
Such raids were organized most skillfully. A number of armed
pirates, looking like ordinary Chinese, would board the boat ostensi-
bly as passengers and then when she was well away from land she
would be overtaken by a pirate vessel whose crew would board the
steamer and with their confederates already on the ship loot cargo
and passengers while the ship's crew did their best to drive off the
attack and make port. Fortunately for us we got to Macao and
back without any such experience, though I felt at the time that
we had unwittingly put our heads into a noose. At Macao, which
is Portuguese and not under Chinese control, we visited an opium

factory and saw the insidious drug being prepared and we also went to a gambling joint. After seeing these sights we wandered about the town, and looked at the buildings public and private. The architecture impressed us as strikingly Portuguese. Though much interested in our trip we returned in the afternoon to Hongkong and felt a certain relief in leaving this region of iniquity and piracy.

On the first of January 1927 we went aboard the *President Lincoln*, and on the second day of the new year we left Hongkong for our long trip over the Pacific to San Francisco and home. We made one day calls at Shanghai, where we picked up our trunks, at Kobe, at Yokohama, and at Honolulu. Our passenger list included a number of those who had gone with us from the states to the Far East: President and Mrs. Wallace W. Atwood of Clark University, Dean and Mrs. D. L. Edsall of the Harvard Medical School, Dr. and Mrs. Victor C. Vaughan of the University of Michigan, and others. On our return voyage, as we dropped anchor for our call at Shanghai, a dozen or so sampans with their Chinese families aboard made for our vessels and tied up at our side under the several sluiceways that came from the kitchens of the ship. Here they spread their nets and caught all the kitchen and dining room refuse that was discharged. I called Dr. Vaughan's attention to a mother who had caught among other things a half-decayed orange. This she had torn open with her hand, rinsed it out in the turbid, yellow river water and was feeding some of it to a small Chinese child. I asked Dr. Vaughan what he thought of this from a hygienic standpoint. He laughed and remarked that while it was not the kind of life that he would advocate he did not think that the germs which would thus be picked up were likely to be pathogenic. I left the situation with the impression that I had learned something about the river life of the Chinese. My wife and I had been most careful about our food during all the time we had been in the orient. We had eaten almost no uncooked vegetables or fruit of any kind, and had insisted in having all our drinking water brought to us as near boiling as possible. Except for one slight indisposition on the part of my wife, we had come through our trip without trouble. When we boarded the *President Lincoln* at Hongkong I asked the ship's doctor what we should do about food and he assured me that we might eat with safety anything that was served us at table, for all the ship's food for the whole voyage out and back had been taken on at San Francisco and refrigerated from there for the whole voyage. It was a delight, that we shall not soon forget, to eat with impunity salads and fruits after having rigorously abstained from them for nearly a half year. We reached San Francisco on time and after a short stop there took the train for the East. We arrived in Boston early in February 1927, occupying the numbered car and stateroom which had been assigned us by ticket before we left home some nine months earlier. I could not help but contrast this American system of travel with the uncertainty of movement that we had met in the orient. Even in Japan the railroad schedules were not always closely observed.

As I look back on our brief visit to China and our longer one to Japan I recognize a pronounced difference in what might be called the national atmospheres of the two countries. China lacked the universal politeness of Japan which, as I have already said, had a certain insincerity about it, but the Chinese showed a directness that had a natural ring to it. When my wife approached a Japanese mother with her baby in her arms she was invariably allowed to see the child and to converse in hand language with both mother and child; when, however, she approached a Chinese mother, the mother would usually withdraw her infant that it might not be influenced by the evil eye, for my wife's eyes were not dark. In Japan the response was politely agreeable; in China it was an assertion of the mother's feelings irrespective of those of the intruder. This self-assertiveness of the Chinese as contrasted with the submissiveness of the Japanese was to me rather refreshing, and since self-assertiveness is an American trait it led me to feel more at home in China than in Japan. Observers have been led to see in this difference an explanation for the general complacency of the Japanese nation as contrasted with the state of civil war which has been so prevalent in China, but in my opinion, as I have already remarked, this is too simple and trivial an explanation.

Since our return from the orient Japan put at least most of her cards on the table and joined with Germany and Italy in a policy of imperialistic expansion. This policy was enforced upon others by military might, irrespective of justice and humane considerations. It was this attitude of the three enemy nations which led to the Second World War, in the settlement of which it is important to recognize exactly what brought about the whole stupendous outbreak. In my opinion the factors in this eruption are biological and concern the growth of populations and the production of food. Neither Italy, Germany, nor Japan can feed its own population from its own soil. The present populations of these countries can be sustained only by additional food supplies from the outside. In brief, these countries are overpopulated. This condition is in strong contrast with that of the United States, for instance, which can maintain its people on the food which it produces within its own borders. If the rest of the world were like the United States no nation would be concerned about expansion. If the rest of the world were like Japan a chaotic struggle for space would everywhere ensue. As one nation after another approaches this condition of overpopulation the expansion of national boundaries and certain changes in internal economy are seized upon as a means of relief, but such a relief is purely temporary for sooner or later the newly acquired territory will become as overpopulated as the original territory. This condition arises inevitably because the power of reproduction in any animal is without limit while the power of the earth to produce food is limited by its total arable surface. Wars such as we have been going through in the First and Second World Wars are warnings to the human race that overpopulation is no longer a matter of theoretic speculation but is a phase of human growth which is beginning to make itself actually felt; in other words the principle of Malthus is being exemplified. No one can view the population-food situation as it exists in Japan and, by contrast, in the United States, without recognizing the gravity of this problem. Some persons have looked forward to a movement that will elevate the standard of living all over the world to that of our country, but it is very doubtful if such a step is at all possible. The momentary maximum food-producing capacity of the total earth would probably not yield enough to enable the world population of today to live as Americans live.

This problem, however, serious as it may be, is by no means insoluble. Its solution depends upon the application of biological discoveries that have been brought to light during the last century or so. In that period great advances were made in our understanding of human reproduction and inheritance. Man is beginning to learn that much of his physical destiny lies in his own hands; that he can, in a certain measure, control his own evolution. This means, so far as the present problem is concerned, that the growth of population is open to limitation. In a measure this has been begun by the western nations where monogamy rather than polygamy has been adopted as a rule of life. The next step is to declare in favor of not only one wife, but of a limited number of offspring, a step that could be adjusted by successive approximations till the number of young born in a nation would produce a population which would be consonant with its food-producing capacity. Such an adjustment would be possible only under some form of world government, but it is precisely this kind of international organization toward which we are at present moving. How this adjustment with its limitation of offspring would be brought about is not to be decided now, but rather to be approached experimentally in course of time. As an alteration in national life it may well come about as did the change from polygamy to monogamy. With help from medical science appropriate laws may well be framed, the final enforcement of which may rest upon some such basis as legal sterilization, a process now current in the majority of our states and especially practiced in California. Thus the way is clear to a possible limitation of populations whereby the relations of peoples to their food supplies may be held at an equitable point. Under such conditions, and particularly if democratic rule prevails, nations will in my opinion cease for the most part in the excesses of war.

XXI

University Life

HE IS PIPING HOT FOR THE UNIVERSITY.
Middleton

TO teach zoology seemed to me a necessary pleasure. By it I expected to earn my bread and butter and by it I hoped to sharpen my wits a bit, for to tell to others what we think we ourselves know is often the best way to discover that we do not know so much as we thought we did. I entered the profession of teaching gradually. In my freshman year at Harvard I began coaching or tutoring students for their examinations. Some of these were college men who had willfully neglected their work and were in dire need of help, and others were men who for one reason or another wished to attain high grades. My tutoring in this first year was all done in elementary botany and zoology. In my sophomore year I added geology and mineralogy to my subjects and I began to be more widely known as a tutor. As a result I easily earned a considerable income, and this was increased in my junior year when I had under my tutelage a considerable number of men, including William Randolph Hearst of whom I have already spoken and John Jacob Astor who, though a man of great natural curiosity and inquisitiveness, lacked the willingness to work hard at the critical moment and consequently failed in many of his academic subjects. That he had real stuff in him was shown at the time of his death, for he helped women and children into lifeboats and then went down himself with the sinking *Titanic* after she struck an iceberg on the North Atlantic in 1912. Also in my junior year I had a small class in natural history in one of the Cambridge private schools, Miss Ingol's School, and here I met for the first time with what might be called ordinary teaching. The two members of this class, Miss Josephine Bumstead and Mrs. T. R. Watson, are still residents of Cambridge and as a matter of fact neighbors of ours. In my senior year I received my first Harvard appointment as laboratory assistant in zoology, and from that time to the present I have been, in one capacity or another, officially connected with the university of my choice. My period of academic teaching at Harvard extended from 1886 to 1935, just one year short of half a century. Since 1935 I have been a professor emeritus.

After having served as laboratory assistant at Harvard for two years I was appointed instructor in 1888 and had full charge of two courses, one on type-animals and the other on the comparative anatomy of vertebrates. Both courses were taken by men who were preparing for medicine or who expected to teach zoology. The course on vertebrates was a third year course and had a number of interesting men in it. One of these was Dr. William E. Ritter, whom I have already mentioned as the organizer of the Scripp's Oceanographic Institute at La Jolla, California. Ritter was my senior by some eight years and always passed himself off as my oldest scholar. He was a marvelous tap dancer and he and I, when on the west coast, amused a camp of Italian workmen by our antics as the men were resting after work on a large dam project in the Sierras. Another early and notable student in vertebrate zoology was Dr. Robert W. Wood, who in after life succeeded to the chair of physics formerly held by Professor Rowland at Hopkins University. Wood was working, along with others in my laboratory, on the spiral valve in the intestine of the skate and had been asked to illustrate it by a sketch; this he was loath to do, for he apparently did not draw easily, but he declared that he could make a model of it with a piece of copper wire and some soapy water. He twisted the wire into an open spiral with one end turned up into the axis of the spiral and then dipped this skeleton form into soapy water and withdrew it. The soap film clung to the spiral and the wire axis and gave in its course an excellent three-dimensional representation of the spiral valve. In all my years of teaching vertebrate anatomy I never before or since had a student who proposed to illustrate the form of the spiral valve in this way. But then I had as a student only one Robert W. Wood. A third worker in the vertebrate course, also very distinguished in his later career, was Dr. Walter B. Cannon. Eventually George Higginson Professor of Physiology in our medical school, Cannon came to Harvard, much as I had done, with very slender financial resources. He first roomed in College

House. Here, as in other dormitories, students heated their own rooms by means of coal grates. In very chilly weather Cannon supplemented his bedding by using newspapers and declared from bitter experience that of all the Boston newspapers the *Evening Transcript* was the warmest. Sad that this sheet has disappeared! All this happened before Cannon, as a young teacher and investigator in the Harvard Medical School, began his remarkable studies on the movements of the digestive organs as disclosed by X-ray shadows, a technique now universally used by clinicians. Cannon, who with his family has long been among our most intimate Cambridge friends, has given us a delightful account of himself in his volume entitled *The Way of an Investigator*.

In this early period I had in sequence two laboratory assistants to help me in the course on type-animals. The first of these was Dr. William A. Setchell, known among his familiars as "Setch." He and I were members of the same class, 1887, he of Yale and I of Harvard. "Setch" was a unique character and very fond of the theater, but he was never able to attend a play with comfort except in the company of at least two friends who understood him and sat one on his right and the other on his left. He was so easily moved to tears and so sensitive about what he took to be a failing that he could not really enjoy a performance without this lateral coöperation. He went, if I remember correctly, several times to *The Iron-Master* which was played by Mr. and Mrs. Kendall and here he shed what seemed to us dangerously large amounts of lachrimal effusions; yet to him it was a deep-seated joy. Setchell transferred eventually to the University of California, where besides his duties in botany he undertook those of dean of men. He was reported to be the best guide to the Barbary Coast of San Francisco, a territory which needed careful watching from the university standpoint. This Setchell gave it. In his scientific work he pointed out the significant and generally overlooked fact that the growth of coral islands was as much a growth of calcareous seaweeds as it was that of coral-forming animals proper.

My second assistant, who followed Setchell by some years, was Herbert Spencer Jennings. Once when asked where he had been educated, Jennings replied, as I recall, "In most states in the Union." His family had been migratory, and he had as a matter of fact gathered his training in a great number of localities. He had a prodigious enthusiasm for his work, which with his native ability carried him to the headship of the zoological department of Johns Hopkins University. Here he developed a remarkable line of work on the responses and inheritance in the one celled animals. True to the traditions of his nomadic ancestors he moved in his full maturity from Baltimore to the California coast.

Later in my academic career I developed and offered several different courses at Harvard, mostly for more mature students and on the lines of my personal researches. This brought me into contact with graduate workers and gave me an opportunity to oversee their investigations and to work with them, an activity which I had long craved. Our studies were, for the most part, on the nervous systems and the nervous reactions of the lower animals, a field of special interest to me. At about the turn of the century I gave up my initial lines of teaching and at the request of the department assumed the management of the large introductory course in zoology, a course intended chiefly for freshmen. I retained, however, my work with graduates, and thus I came to see in these two lines of teaching the beginning and the end so to speak of our efforts in academic zoology. The contrast was most striking. The beginner in the subject often exhibited unexpected enthusiasms, commonly misdirected and even grotesque but nevertheless real enthusiasms; these seemed to me to call for guidance rather than suppression, the latter a treatment so often given them by the "superior" teacher. The graduate student, though mature and often rich in experience, appeared to have lost what enthusiasm he may have had as a beginner and to be devoid of the spontaneous interest which might be expected in a growing scholar. I asked myself, is this the result of our method of teaching or do young men at this stage naturally arrive at a kind of sophistication which is detrimental to their real advancement? It seemed as though their original enthusiasms had been schooled out of them. I could not help but contrast their lifelessness, if I may so describe their attitude, with the real though often misdirected interest that many of them showed as beginners. In thinking on this matter I continually returned to parallelism of the boundless enthusiasm over very commonplace things which children so often show, and how they exhaust their elders with questions on these matters. What I mean is well illustrated by an occurrence in front of the Agassiz Museum on Oxford Street, Cambridge. A mother was leading a small child, as she had probably done scores of times, by the drive from the street onto the museum grounds. The gate at this entrance was almost always open, but this time it was closed. The child had probably never seen it closed before and burst out, "Mother, Mother, the gate, the gate, it's closed. Why is it closed?" The poor mother was drawing the child onward and I stopped and said to the youngster, "Don't you see, the men are putting coal in the museum cellar and they do not want the road blocked by other teams while they are at work and so they have closed the gate." The child looked into the grounds, saw the men at work on the coal, and seemed satisfied and as the mother and youngster were about to move on, the mother said to me rather pathetically, "Thank you for one question answered." As I thought the situation over I could not suppress the feeling that if our graduates had only retained some of this eternal questioning of youth how close they would be to their goal. Does our present system of university training crush in most students the spirit of enthusiastic inquiry? I suspect it does.

It is not to be supposed that every college man is cut out to be a profound scholar in his subject, but it is fair to expect that the training which he undergoes ought not to block his progress toward some reasonable end. To facilitate this progress two conditions are probably essential in university organization: the reduction of restrictive regulations to a minimum and the granting to the student of great personal freedom of action, if these two really are separate affairs. Restrictive regulations are almost always the outcome of experience with incompetent students; they are devised to pull the poor man up to the level of the good man. But by so doing they often hamper the good man so that he cannot do his best. The regulation is unfortunately made to apply to him, irrespective of whether it is the best thing for him or not. It is often difficult to make university administrators see that regulations should be made from the standpoint of what is best for the good student rather than for what is needed for the poor one. Do not let the poor student hamper the good one. Let the incompetent drop by the side. It is better to give the best men every chance than to handicap them because of their weak brothers.

The second feature in advancing the growth of university students is the granting to them of as much freedom of action as possible. If the student is a worthwhile man, he will use that freedom well; if he is not worthwhile, why trouble about him? Let him take the consequences. In other words, to use an old phrase slightly changed, give the student liberty or give him death. It was my plan in teaching to extend liberty to students as far as I could reasonably do so. To this end I often ignored petty office regulations. The lecturers in the larger college courses at Harvard were from time to time requested to close and catch their classroom doors at the beginning of a lecture, and thus to exclude tardy auditors. I felt that I was there to teach zoology and I believed that a half hour of zoology was better for a student than no zoology at all. Hence I always omitted to carry out this office request. I was never annoyed, as some instructors claimed to have been, by late arrivals. When tardy students did come to the class they invariably slipped into the room noiselessly and took any vacant place without disturbance.

The reduction of college regulations to a minimum and the extension to the student of the greatest reasonable liberty were to me two closely related features which helped in a small way toward retaining the interest of a student in a subject and in preventing the evaporation of his early enthusiasms. Under these conditions, and with a live teacher, the subject ought to grow upon him and eventually mature in him with his original interests properly directed and intensified. John Muir had this in mind when in discussing education he declared, "Nourish youth's enthusiasms which in society die untimely." The principles here advocated by me would of course be abused, but what educational scheme is free from abuse of one kind or another? In my opinion it is wiser on the whole to give a George Santayana a chance to grow fully than to save for uncertain academic association a score of semi-incompetents. I agree fully with many of those interested in the best form of university organization when I plead for the preservation and cultivation of the youthful enthusiasms as contrasted with what too often happens, their partial or even complete extinction.

In the kind of life I had taken up at Harvard I naturally made many acquaintances with other university colleagues whose paths crossed mine. In this way I frequently walked half a mile or so with Dr. T. W. Richards of the chemical laboratory as we made our ways home to luncheon or other engagements. Richards was a man of wide interests and showed a keen enthusiasm over many chemical problems in my experimental work on animals. Though ever mindful of an orderly plan in the universe Richards never lost sight of the material properties of nature, and thus he kept in view those extremes in the world about him which saved him from a narrow outlook. For a biologist, Richards's opinions were full of profitable suggestions. I also profited by conversation with my neighbor, Dr. G. W. Pierce, of the Jefferson Physical Laboratory. Pierce was an inimitable and ready raconteur of most appropriate tales which he would willfully turn now this way, now that, to fit the circumstances. I shall not soon forget his comment on meeting me on the street one spring day after I had been suffering from a carbuncle on my neck. Pierce remarked that my blood must have been very poor to have laid me open to such an attack. I told him that attacks of this kind depended not so much on poor blood as on the presence of certain disease germs near the hair follicles on my neck. He was much interested and asked me rather naïvely whether if I had kept my neck perfectly clean I would have avoided the carbuncle; I was forced to answer in the affirmative. After a moment's thought Pierce remarked that the circumstances made clear to him what he had often heard his grandmother say, "A washed spot never boils." Could a joking reply have been more spontaneous! With such a wit a lecture by Pierce even on the driest physics must have been a lively affair; and even his most serious discussions never lacked this jovial humor.

In 1917 the United States entered the First World War. What could a zoologist do to advance our national effort? Physicians were urgently called for and in the preparation of young men for the medical profession our department had a program to meet their needs. We each took on some extra teaching, readjusted some of our courses, and arranged a revised schedule which would enable any young man to complete his pre-medical work in zoology in one year instead of two. Several of us rather unofficially took up problems immediately connected with war work. My interest in marine animals led me to investigate paints that might prevent the growth of organisms on ship bottoms. Naval vessels may lose as much as ten percent of their speed in consequence of the growth of animals and plants on their hulls. Some of the results of my research, I trust, helped make better paints for this purpose than those that were already in use. At least certain of our newly devised mixtures were composed of substances whose accessibility was much greater than those used in the older paints; copper salts were substituted for the rarer mercuric compounds to advantage.

In 1921 I was appointed to serve as exchange professor to the western colleges and in February of that year I began my new service by lecturing for a month at Grinnell College, Iowa. The zoologist at Grinnell was my old friend Dr. Harry W. Norris, and it was a great pleasure for me to meet and lecture to his classes. I was asked by heads of other departments at Grinnell to speak to their classes, and I had resolved to meet such requests as fully as possible, a resolve that often put me under no small strain. I often found myself in novel situations. During the month that I spent at Grinnell I gave four public lectures at the morning periods known as "Long Chapel." The lecture was preceded by prayer, offered usually by one of the faculty members whose subject was nearly related to what I was to talk about. At the close of my lecture there was often some congregational singing, after which a brief prayer closed the exercise. It all appeared to me to be very incongruous, but then perhaps I was too sophisticated. At the close of the exercise a professor was often in waiting at the door of the chapel with the request that I speak to such and such a class which was then being held for me, and such a request might be repeated at the end of my second talk. I remember once having been asked in the first hour after my chapel address to speak to a class in fine arts and at the close of this impromptu lecture to be invited to another in psychology. I was near exhaustion in the midst of my psychological effort and consequently at the end of half an hour with this class I ceased speaking and asked the members present to supplement my remarks by putting questions to me. I had a very encouraging and helpful response. Finally a young Negro student asked me what was my idea of the life to come. In reply I told him that I was a scientific man and thought and talked in a descriptive way only about things that I had actually experienced. I added that as he must know, I, like most other persons, had thus far had no real contact with the world beyond and that in consequence I abstained from forming precise opinions about such matters till I had outlived this life. I do not believe that what I said satisfied this young Negro at all, but it at least gave him some idea of the way many people felt about the question that he had raised. Grinnell proved to be a great stimulus to me and its youthful, buoyant, and enthusiastic students infected me with a wish to stay longer with them, but my time was drawing to an end. From Grinnell I went to Colorado College at Colorado Springs where, on the eastern edge of the Rocky Mountains, I began to know something of "where the West begins." My wife joined me there but before she arrived I was put up for a time at the El Paso Club where several town residents were staying. One of these, a very capable artist, commonly took breakfast with me. It soon became evident that he, like most of his class, was always in need of funds. He described his condition to me in terms that I had never before heard used, for he told me with a pathetic smile that he was forced to live on the interest on his debts.

From Colorado Springs my wife and I took the train to Santa Fe, the capital of New Mexico, where we had a week of interesting experiences. By advice at the railroad station we took rooms and board in a Catholic hospital for tubercular patients where the Sister Superior was most kind and considerate. We wandered about town, saw the oldest house built by Europeans in the United States, and visited Sig. Candelario's Trading Post where we were very kindly entertained and shown some beautiful Indian work in silver, basketry, blankets, and the like. We learned from Sig. Candelario that he was the last of his name, descendant of a direct line of ancestors who had lived in the same place since the coming of the Spanish fathers. When we told the Sister Superior these things she listened to us with reserve and then, after some *sub rosa* remarks about lying, told us that our Mexican romancer had bought the place where he now was some three years before. We nevertheless continued to call on Sig. Candelario and enjoyed his remarkable elaborations, but we kept to ourselves the truth told us by the Sister Superior.

Through the advice of this interesting woman we took a day's drive over the desert to the Pueblo of San Domingo in the valley of the Rio Grande. Here we witnessed an Indian rain dance which was to last through the week and which was intended to induce the fall of rain on the adjacent mountains whence came the water that moistened the growing crops of these agricultural Indians. It was indeed an astounding spectacle, as one body of dancers replaced another to the chanting and tom-tom accompaniment of a chorus standing in the center of the open pueblo. As my wife looked on at this unusual show she noticed an Indian with strings of shell beads and rough turquoises about his neck. We asked our chauffeur if such could be bought in the pueblo. He assured us that the young Indian near us would sell them directly off his neck. We had difficulty in making him understand our wishes, for he spoke only his own dialect and no Spanish or English. Finally it appeared that he would sell four strings of beads for twelve dollars. But we wished only one. Then after much palaver it seemed that he was willing to sell two for six dollars. Again we declared for only one string and he in the end asked for this one two dollars and a half; he maintained that two strings *paired* were worth more than twice one *single*, for the pairing of strings was not an easy matter. This seemed to us strange logic, but he would not accept more than the two and a half dollars for the single string, and so with a kind of reluctance we closed the bargain.

On our return to the hospital we told the Sister what we had seen and that a priest with a little chapel near the pueblo had assured us that all the Indians there had been baptized and were fully christianized. "But," said I, "they are dancing this week to strange gods and asking them for rain." "Yes!" said the Sister, "and we Catholics are not yet under their skins." We left Santa Fe with regret and with a feeling that the Sister Superior of the Tuberculosis Hospital was rather the wisest of those whose acquaintances we had made there. From Santa Fe we went by train to the Grand Canyon where we enjoyed a week of climbing and sightseeing, and then again by train to the coastal lands of California where I served the last of my three college missions as exchange professor at Pomona College.

Here was a thriving biological center under Professor W. A. Hilton, who also conducted a small seaside laboratory at Laguna Beach on the Pacific shore. Leaving the canyon and the cold and snow behind us in the mountains we had suddenly emerged into a semi-tropical land of orange groves in full blossom and fruitage. The change was unbelievable, as are most such things in California! Again interesting audiences, generous hospitality, and delightful excursions into the surrounding countryside! Two desert men who were in charge of a desert ranch drove a small party of us for a three day trip out onto the desert beyond Palm Springs and within sight of the Salton Sea. These men knew the water holes on the desert and how and where to camp. We carried blankets with us and slept in our clothes on the ground. The desert was beautiful in its spring blossoms. Some of our expedition were botanists, but one was a zoologist and was collecting rattlesnake skins for a local museum. He had excellent success, but our desert guides could not see the meat of the dead snakes go to waste. So at several of our meals we cooked the snake meat over our fire and ate it. I found it more than palatable. To my taste it seemed rather like frogs' legs, though on the whole better. The desert sunrises and sunsets with the distant Salton Sea in view or the occasional groups of tall palms around some water hole have left memories in my mind never to be erased. Thus ended for me a most stimulating episode in my academic life, that of serving as an exchange professor to the western colleges. Some years later as I was passing through the Harvard Yard I met President Blaisdell of Pomona College. We greeted each other cordially after which he remarked, "We keep your grave green in Pomona." What could I say! But when I recalled how difficult it had been to obtain an adequate water supply for the town in which Pomona is located, Claremont, I acknowledged the implied compliment and thanked him for the imaginary attention.

XXII

New Life and New Laboratories

WITH LOADS OF LEARNED LUMBER IN HIS HEAD.

Pope

IN 1909, because of the proposed withdrawal of one of the older Harvard teachers in botany, it was planned to seek a new man for this post and the university was fortunate enough to obtain the services for this position of Dr. W. J. V. Osterhout who was called for this purpose from the University of California. With this teacher and investigator I found many points of common interest. Osterhout was born in Brooklyn, New York, in 1871, had been trained at Brown University and in Europe and had finally settled at the University of California in Berkeley whence he came to us. His family consisted of his wife and two daughters, Anna and Olga. All were excellent walkers and enjoyed the open country. In California the daughters had had very little experience with what would be called New England winter weather, for, excepting in the Californian mountains, they had seen very little snow and ice. Dr. Osterhout from his early associations knew this kind of climate and looked forward to an enjoyment of it in and about Cambridge. Shortly after his arrival at Harvard I invited him some days in advance for a walk in the country. The day appointed was inclement with some hail and rain. I nevertheless went to the Osterhout house, expecting that the walk would be called off. On the contrary I found Dr. Osterhout dressed for bad weather and ready to go. We had a beautiful, long walk through the country to the west of Cambridge in an atmosphere of occasional snow and hail such as Dr. Osterhout had missed ever since he had been in California. To him it was real New England and he enjoyed it quite as much as I did, for such weather was to my liking. This gave me a sample of what Dr. Osterhout, an old New Englander, longed for. On another occasion in the late autumn he and I took a Sunday morning walk over the Arlington hills and in a rocky park we came upon a small, shallow pond of a few acres' extent that because of its shallowness had early frozen over. Already a number of Arlington boys and girls were skating on it. I saw at once what was in Winthrop Osterhout's head. That afternoon Anna and Olga with their skates and equipment were conducted by their father to the Belmont pond where they engaged in their first New England skating. Thus the excitement of winter at home gradually dawned on the Osterhout family. The first real snow in Cambridge was watched for by them with feverish anticipation. And what a snow it was! It began in the evening and the next morning the whole landscape was covered with six to eight inches of light, fluffy needles of clean, white snow. What a transformation it gave to everything! The bare trees were outlined in snow, the fences and garden gates were masquerading in new forms, the small evergreens were covered with snow and their branches were bent down to give all the appearance of an Indian wigwam. Nature had taken on an entirely new aspect, and what an astounding one! I believe I never saw before or since a more charming New England snowstorm. I did not dare tell the Osterhout girls how exceptional it was. I let them enjoy it for its own worth. They could not have been given a finer introduction to a New England snow. And so the winter went with a riot of weather. May it remain with them always as a dream of youth.

Winthrop Osterhout was interested in many other things than the New England countryside, fascinating as that was to him. I took him on a shopping tour one day among the oriental booths of Chinatown. It was my intention to gather for my wife a dozen Medallion plates on no two of which the ornamentation would be the same, and to do this I planned to inspect the stock of a goodly number of Chinese stores. We went to endless such establishments till finally my quest was completed. I soon found that Winthrop was as much interested in this search as I was. We then had Italian coffee together at an Italian café in the North End and the shopping tour was finished. Winthrop summed up the afternoon's perform- ance by a remark on the way home, "And now I have seen Boston," in such a tone that I knew he would be open to a second invitation. In that way our wanderings began about town, wanderings

which always had some definite object in view though at times
they might do little more than terminate in a luncheon at an
Italian café.

One discovery I soon made about Winthrop and that was that
he had brought several California habits with him. One of these
was always to rely on "his wad." This was his roll of bank bills
which he regularly carried in his trousers pocket. If we went to an
Italian restaurant for luncheon, as for instance the Stella d'Italia,
Winthrop would always toward the end of the meal bring out his
wad and endeavor to pay the bill. I had great difficulty in making
it clear to him that for the first year in Boston he was always a
guest. To impress this upon him I finally invited him to a few hours
in Boston including a luncheon which I had prearranged. The
luncheon was to be at John Leveroni's on North Street in the North
End. Here I went and agreed with the waiter that I should pay in
advance for the whole meal and that the waiter should make such
reply to Dr. Osterhout when near the conclusion of the meal my
guest would propose to pay for our repast. When our luncheon,
which had been a very good one, was drawing to a close, I saw
Winthrop reach for his wad and call the waiter. As Winthrop
asked for the bill, the waiter politely bowed and said, "Oh, Sir,
there is no charge at this restaurant for luncheon." Winthrop
looked first at the waiter and then at me and as he saw a smile
break out on my face he waved his hand toward me as a sign that
I had trapped him. I never succeeded by such means as this in
blocking Winthrop's generous impulses, for they were more inbred
than California could have induced in him, but I did finally get
him to be a little more reasonable with his wad than he was on first
arrival. However, as a companion to walk with over the countryside or as one to go about town with I always ranked him as a
Prince of Fellows and it was with the utmost regret that I saw him
and his family leave us for New York in 1925.

While I was lecturing on zoology at Harvard I was forced to use
many unfamiliar and long names for animals or for their parts. I
told the class that when I used such terms I would as a rule spell
them or write them out on the blackboard. If, for any reason,
members of the class failed to get a given name, I advised them to
write in their notes any combination of letters that seemed to represent the sound of the term and to look it up afterwards in a

textbook or, failing that, to bring it to me for identification. I naturally had many strange combinations, some of which were real "boners." One student once submitted to me a page of notes on which he had written here and there "a kind of tomato." I puzzled out the context and it appeared that the word he was trying to imitate was Echinodermata, the name of the group of animals containing the starfishes, sea urchins, and the like. Another student made a real boner in his examination paper where he declared in defining a marsupial that it was a mammal the female of which had a pouch on its abdomen and "when it was scared it jumped in." The student who told me in naming the animal characteristic of South America that that land abounded in peccadillos received a full grade, for his combination word covered peccaries and armadillos, both of which are peculiar to America south of Mexico. These are a few of the bright spots in examination testing.

I often spoke to students about their English reading and asked them what classic texts they kept near them. I was surprised to find that few Harvard men kept up their English classics at all. Few, if any, read the foreign classics in translation and Shakespeare and Chaucer scarcely at all. It seemed to me a shocking indifference to their native tongue. They were not illiterate and yet knowing their language they failed to use it. We should have some term between literate and illiterate to indicate such shocking neglect. No college graduate should pass through life without acquiring the reading habit for at least his own tongue.

Our laboratories were from time to time subject to the visitation of foreign scholars. They came as exchange professors or otherwise and brought with them a breath of the outer air. The first I remember was Professor W. Kükenthal from Breslau. He spent much of 1912 with us and lectured in English with great effect to the elementary class. He had spent two years with the Arctic whaling fleet and was full of interesting anecdotes. Soon after him, in 1916, came Professor M. Caullery from Paris whose lectures in French on the general characteristics of animals were a beautiful example of what the best French lecturing could be. In 1929 Professor A. Brachet and his wife made us a good-will visit of two weeks or so. Professor Brachet gave us several very enjoyable lectures on embryology in French. He came to us just as the discussion about our new laboratory was at its height and before we had the means to build

it. He and I talked much about our prospects. At the end of one of these conferences he said to me, "And if you had what you want, what would it be?" I told him without hesitation an ample and well-furnished new laboratory with a properly equipped and manned section for general physiology. He put his hand on my shoulder and added, "You will get it. You Americans always get what you strive after." Little did I think at that time that in some three years our wishes would be realized!

While I was in California as exchange professor, in the spring of 1921, I was appointed director of the Harvard Zoological Laboratory. On returning to Cambridge that autumn I took up a new and additional set of duties. When I had at first begun teaching zoology at Harvard in 1888 the subject was a part of Natural Science and all the formal instruction in it was given by two persons, Professor E. L. Mark and myself. After I became director of the Laboratory in 1921 the department of zoology included six instructors, and when I resigned the directorship in 1934 there were in all about a score of teachers in zoology. This very considerable increase in the teaching force was in part due to the encouragement given to laboratory sciences by President Eliot and President Lowell, and in part due to group reorganization especially under President Lowell. President Lowell favored in his administration the consolidation of subjects, and therefore resolved to transfer the biology taught at the Bussey Institution in Forest Hills to Cambridge. By this step the Cambridge group of zoologists was increased by some six additional members. Moreover, through the generosity of the director of the Museum of Comparative Zoölogy, Mr. Samuel Henshaw, seven of the curators in the museum were allowed to offer courses in their special fields of study, and thus to receive as students advanced men from the department of zoology. In this way the department increased its total teaching force by about a dozen and greatly enriched its offerings in instruction. Thus the whole number of instructors in zoology finally reached a score without materially changing our budget. By combining the zoologists from three more or less independent centers, the zoological department, the Bussey Institution, and the museum, President Lowell had in view not merely a simplification of university organization, but an intensification of the zoological effort by bringing together, to the advantage of all, three bodies of scientific workers originally somewhat separated. No one, except perhaps the President, saw the importance of this step till it had been on trial some years and its great advantages began to appear in the increased and advantageous associations of zoologists, botanists, and physiologists. Then indeed the real significance of biology as a science of living things began to be seen and President Lowell's ideas started to bear fruit.

It must not be supposed that the reorganization of biological interests briefly outlined in the last paragraph as having occurred in the two decades preceding 1935 took place without full consideration. We all had much to say about it. One very important member of the department who took part in these discussions was Winthrop Osterhout, already referred to in this chapter. Osterhout was interested in the physiological side of botany and supported several of us in the belief that part of the laboratory work in biology should be made up of simple experiments on living organisms. Both Osterhout and I had already tried out a number of simple tests on living plants and animals in our own laboratories to assure ourselves that such tests were really serviceable as laboratory exercises. In zoology the feeding responses of toads and of smaller fresh water fishes, the reactions of insects and of earthworms to lights and to odorous substances in their surroundings, and many other such types of simple activities among these lower creatures, afforded the kinds of tests that could be worked upon as means of understanding animal movements. Trials of this kind called for endless ingenuity on the part of inquisitive students and led them to an interpretation of the operations of lower animals which afforded a basis for the understanding of the responses of living creatures from the lowest to the highest. But such a program called for the means of keeping living stocks of plants and animals on hand, and for a laboratory system quite unlike that with which we were then supplied. When these matters were brought to the attention of the President and the overseers the need for new laboratories and equipment became at once apparent and several of the college officers, and especially President Lowell, entered heartily into the plan for a new biological laboratory. This was to be built near the museum so that the collections and the library in that institution could be easily available and yet so separated that the hazard of laboratory fire would be eliminated. Such a laboratory should be fireproof, composed of many small rooms that might be used as section laboratories, more fully equipped laboratories for advanced work, and workrooms of the professors under whose guidance the general research of the institution would progress. It must be equipped with ample hothouse facilities for the cultivation of plants, and rooms for the accommodation and breeding of stocks of animals large and small. Moreover, these laboratories should be kept open day and night so that all advanced students could have access to them at any hour that their work demanded. During the day the laboratories should be freely open and during the evening and night access to them should be granted to any properly qualified person by the custodian in general charge of the building. Thus a laboratory was planned, the central object of which was biological research and the training leading thereto, and with an organization that would put a minimum of inconvenience in the way of any serious, advanced student. To plan a university laboratory, the uses of which may extend over half a century or more, is no small task. What laboratory director can know in what direction in the next decade or two his science will grow? About the beginning of this century physics was regarded as a nearly finished field, but who could have ever surmised the tremendous advances that have come into it since that time. Scientific prediction seems to be about as uncertain as that on the weather.

This plan for a biological laboratory was submitted by those who devised it to many of the workers who would be expected to occupy the building as well as to President Lowell and to others in authority with the result that it gained in general the approval of all concerned. In one respect were we handicapped. In 1925 Professor Osterhout, who had been one of the prime movers for the new laboratory, was called away by an appointment at the Rockefeller Institute for Medical Research in New York, and thus we lost from our midst a person whose advice and counsel meant more than that of any other individual interested in the new project. Fortunately Dr. Osterhout, notwithstanding his removal, retained to the full his interest in our plans and aided us in many ways in our subsequent steps. The new laboratories were to house physiologists, zoologists, and botanists. The details of the plans for the physiologists were to be worked out by Dr. W. J. Crozier and his associates, for the zoologists by Dr. L. Hoadley, Dr. W. M. Wheeler, and Professor C. T. Brues, and for the botanists by Dr. R. H. Wetmore and others.

The plans for each of the sections in the laboratories were soon matured and after they had received general approval steps were initiated to find the means whereby the laboratories could be constructed. It soon became voiced abroad that Harvard had outgrown its present biological accommodations, that it had a good set of plans for the construction of new laboratories, and that it was seeking funds with which to build the new housing for its biological work. Several of the larger foundations looked over the Harvard situation with care and admitted that the university was in dire need of a modernized biological outfit. Finally the matter was brought to the attention of the International Education Board by Professor Harlow Shapley and Professor Oakes Ames, and through the generosity of this board a proposal was made to the Harvard Corporation which would enable that body to build and equip suitable laboratories. These laboratories were finally erected on the east side of Divinity Avenue, directly opposite the university museum, and they included the principal workshops of the department of biology. They were assigned an ample endowment by the Harvard Corporation. They were first opened in the autumn of 1931 and since then have been devoted primarily to research and instruction in botany, zoology, and physiology. They are fully equipped with shops, photographic appliances, dark rooms, constant-temperature rooms, aquaria, animal rooms, and greenhouses and contain a range of larger and smaller laboratories where investigators may work singly or in small groups under conditions favorable to their special needs. The building contains a considerable reference library and is within easy reach of the much larger collections of books in the Museum of Comparative Zoölogy, in the Mallinckrodt Chemical Laboratory, and in the Farlow Herbarium. Thus the Harvard biological laboratories are well situated for library facilities and have come to house much of the Harvard experimental biological work which was formerly scattered over a wider space in and about Cambridge.

During the building of the laboratories few days went by when President Lowell and his little dog, Phantom, did not walk over the newly constructed parts of the building and see that plans had been followed. In fact the laboratories may be said to have been built strictly under the President's eye. The laboratories have the form of a large letter E, with the concavity of the letter facing the museum. They are of red brick with ample window space and the upper brick surfaces are covered lightly with the outlines of animals. The three main doors are ornamented with conventional forms representing the organisms of the air, the sea, and the land; and the sides of the doors are guarded by two massive bronzes, African rhinos, which together with the other ornamentation on the building are the work of the well-known artist, Miss Katharine W. Lane. It is an open question which of the many college buildings put up under President Lowell's administration attracts the most attention. Considering the number of visitors who come to see the biological laboratories the biologists are inclined to think that their building ranks near the top. It certainly excites a wide range of interest. In favorable weather children take great delight in climbing over the backs of the rhinos, and dogs never pass these bronze giants without stopping for a volley of salutes. The rhinos certainly appeal in different ways to a large section of the Cambridge population. Miss Lane had such an affection for the rhinos that she named them, both females, after the English queens. The rhino at the south of the entrance she called Bess after Queen Elizabeth and the one to the north Vic after Queen Victoria. Thus the biology building sports a royal entrance.

The biological laboratories as a whole are very uniformly constructed and consist of a basement carrying over it five stories of research rooms. Each story measures in length over its central hallway some 685 feet. It is a remarkable fact that this very large building was put up in the course of some two years without the loss of a workman's life; in fact, without even a serious injury to a single employee, a record not often achieved in any such extensive building project. This is a source of great satisfaction to those who have kept it in mind and who have since made use of the laboratories. The biological laboratories had their workrooms next to the outer walls that they might have plenty of window space and their halls central in position and artificially lighted. The rooms are in sizes single-, double-, or triple-unit rooms separated by thin, easily removable partitions, a feature that has been found very convenient in the slight remodeling which the interior of the building has required. When the laboratories were under construction, President Lowell found that his funds not only would allow of the building of the south wing and the central body of the structure but also a large part of the north wing. This addition was not assigned to biology, but was held in reserve. It was temporarily occupied by the Rindge Technical School of Cambridge during a period in which a new city school building was under construction. During the Second World War it was fully used by a United States Radio Research Laboratory. Thus the north wing of our laboratories has for some time past served for important but nonacademic activities.

The new building has been in service nearly fifteen years and during this period it has contributed to the training of a large number of investigators and has enabled its permanent staff to publish a continuous flow of research. It would be premature to estimate the value of such a combination. In the erection of the laboratory the best plans available were followed and these have proved to be plastic enough for all innovations thus far needed. President Lowell's general views for a union of biological laboratories have proved to be fully justified and what were originally three somewhat separate groups of investigators in zoology, in botany, and in physiology are now fused into a single group of biologists whose endeavors have much in common. This unification is a small part of what the biological laboratory has contributed toward the proper advance in the study of living animals and plants at Harvard.

XXIII

Relaxation

AND THE PEOPLE SAT DOWN TO EAT AND
TO DRINK AND ROSE UP TO PLAY.

Exodus, 32:6

NO one can keep up the pace of a university teacher and investigator without an occasional bit of relaxation. In my past experience the most easygoing place was Italy and now in America I found its duplicate, perhaps unconsciously, in Boston's Little Italy in the North End. Before the First World War I went from time to time to an Italian restaurant, the Napoli, in the north of Boston, where for fifty cents in those inexpensive days a simple Italian luncheon with a quinto of California red wine could be had. After a *pourboire* of ten cents to the waiter the price of the whole was not an extravagant amount even for an underpaid Harvard teacher. I formed the acquaintance at the Napoli of an excellent Italian waiter who had been brought up near Naples, and who consequently knew much to talk about that revived my memories of that most interesting and fascinating place. It did not matter how greatly I had been pressed by work or how disturbing my circumstances might have been, the moment I entered the Napoli I passed into a quiet and carefree atmosphere and after its simple Italian meal, stretched over an hour or so, ending with a *caffè nero* and a cigarette or two, life took on a very different tone. But all good things come to an end and with the demise of the proprietor of the Napoli this resort passed out of existence. Even the building was torn down. Thus my refuge from the undue pressure of American life disappeared. In this emergency a former student and old friend, Dr. H. V. Neal of Tufts College, came to my rescue and led me one day to the Capri, a small Italian combined club and restaurant in the very heart of Little Italy. Here the atmosphere was, if possible, still more Neapolitan than at the Napoli itself.

The Capri occupied the second floor of a house on one of the busiest streets in Little Italy. It looked out on a beehive of grocery shops, apothecaries', cafés, and the like, and with the throngs of Italian men and women passing up and down and stopping to exchange gossip and with innumerable children playing about, it might well have been in any Neapolitan side street such as I remembered so well. Here indeed I found again balm to my soul and a release from my daily academic strains. How providential of Neal to have brought me to the Capri!

I really became first acquainted with this semi-club and its proprietor on one early spring Sunday, after I had been to this resort several times during the previous winter. On that Sunday I had had a long walk in the Middlesex Fells and I was on my way through Boston to Cambridge. As it was early afternoon it occurred to me to take a late midday meal at the Capri. I entered, enjoyed a good plate of spaghetti, followed by some scolapini, ba-ba, and a caffè. When I asked the proprietor, who was on the floor and had served me, for my bill, he smiled and said there was none. I looked surprised and he added, "Do you not know what day this is?" I replied that it was Easter Sunday, to which he added, "Think what was once given us on this day. Anyone may have food in this place today and there will be no charge." I bowed my acknowledgment and thanks. I then noticed that his two helpers were putting the small tables together in a long row, setting chairs and places for guests, and in other ways preparing for a number of diners. I thought the least I could do was to help, and so in my poor way I lent a hand at the task till it was finished. Thereupon the proprietor, who had been working with us, asked me to sit down with him and have a small portion of homemade Italian wine. Here we chatted for a time over his home product. He told me that his name was Aristeo Passananti, that he came from a small town near Salerno in southern Italy, and that he had established himself in Boston with Neapolitan kitchen helpers to open a combination club and restaurant for those of his countrymen and their families who wished such food as he could provide after the Neapolitan manner. I explained to him that I had been for half a year a student at the Naples Aquario, which he knew very well, and that I was greatly attracted by the atmosphere of his establishment and the flavor of his kitchen. We parted with mutual signs of esteem and I promised to visit the Capri again. I found on my repeated returns to this restaurant that I had become in a measure a member of its kindly group, for Aristeo always met me most cordially and usually attended personally to my wants.

In the course of time I picked up much about Aristeo's life. His father had been mayor of the small Italian town of Serra Persano near Salerno when Aristeo had been born. As a young man he was supposed to succeed to his father's place. He therefore studied law and otherwise prepared himself for what he supposed would be his future duties. Meanwhile he had fallen in love with a young woman of estimable family and they had become engaged. Shortly after this the lady of his choice was overtaken by a serious illness and died. From this pathetic loss Aristeo never fully recovered, and from that time onward he led a life of strict celibacy. Always very kindly and considerate of the opposite sex, whether young or old, he was never known to make advances toward them. But this was not the only trial which befell Aristeo as a young man. At about this time King Humbert of Italy was assassinated, and assassinated by a man who carried the same family name as Aristeo. As a result Aristeo could not be considered as mayor for his native place, though he was in no way concerned with the crime. His chief prospects blasted, he left Italy and came to America. Here he settled in Boston, and after having been unsuccessful in attempts to enter the law he opened the Capri.

Aristeo was a man well educated in his way and well read. Whenever I came to the Capri I was sure to have an interesting quarter of an hour with him during my meal in which we would talk over the thousand and one topics which might occur to a native and to a confirmed admirer of his beloved Naples. During these tête-à-têtes he was sure to mention a dozen pleasantries, and thus add to the delight of my meal. I often told him that all that was needed to make such occasions perfect was to look out of the windows of his restaurant onto the beautiful Gulf of Salerno instead of the prosaic North End street, Italian in appearance though it was. I frequented the Capri during our period of national prohibition and I was always treated by Aristeo to a portion of homemade red wine served in a coffee cup. For this addition to my repast he would never make a charge, for he knew the law and that he might legally make and give away wine but not sell or transport it. When one day he was about to serve me with his homemade vintage he remarked, "Il vino è la late dei vecchi"—"wine is the milk of old age"—to which I assented. He was a quick hand at Italian phrases and once gave me a sentence which could be construed either in Latin or in Italian, but with very different meanings, "I vitelli sono belli" which in the language of Caesar means, "Go Vittellus to the sound of war" and in that of Dante, "The calves are beautiful." Such *jeu d'esprit* were common occurrences with Aristeo. But he was not all playfulness. He was infinitely kind. Many a time have I seen him conduct a miserably poor Italian from the door of the restaurant to the kitchen and provide him with a plate full of hot food. Yet so far as I know he was never imposed upon. Only the truly needy knocked at his gate. To these and to his many patrons he was a beneficent and kindly host. Some ten years ago I was called to my telephone in the Harvard laboratory and told by one of Aristeo's helpers that he had just suffered a paralytic stroke and that he was believed to be near death's door. I went at once to the Capri over which he lived, found him in bed, still conscious, but very much incapacitated. He recognized me and we had a few kindly words. A week or so later I attended his funeral in an Italian chapel in the vicinity of North Square. Thus passed from our midst a generous, earnest, sincere soul whose honest simplicity was that of a child.

Among my Harvard colleagues in those interbellum days was my old friend, Dr. William M. Wheeler, who had been a worker at the Naples zoological station, a little before my time there. He, too, had imbibed a taste for Neapolitan life and when I took him to the Capri as a sample of Little Italy he fell in with it at once. Here he and I came quite regularly for weekly midday repasts, after which we would spend the early afternoon in shopping or the like in Boston before we returned to Cambridge. Shortly after this time our mutual friend, Dr. E. B. Holt, took us to another Italian restaurant, this time in the Back Bay, at Technology Chambers, where a good Italian menu was always to be had. After this introduction we commonly alternated between the Capri and our newly discovered rendezvous in the Back Bay. This establishment, however, soon fell into disrepute with the police during our national prohibition and was closed. At Technology Chambers we were regularly served by an Italian waiter of very unusual ability and kindliness known to all of us as Joe. On the dissolution of the restaurant we lost sight of him for a while, but eventually I received a post card addressed to Dr. Parker, Harvard College, etc., and stating that Joe was now at the Amalfi on Westland Avenue, where, as he expressed it, they had everything that was good for man and beast. Wheeler and I made our way to this resort and found that Joe's description of the place met our anticipations. Here was an exceptionally good Italian menu and here, moreover, was Joe with all his kindly attentions. At about this time Aristeo of the Capri passed away and the Capri itself declined and disappeared. Hence we were obliged to content ourselves with the Amalfi. Here we two consorted rather regularly. Wheeler, who was always given to scholarly performances, insisted that at these agreeable outings there should be food for the soul as well as for the body. He therefore declared for some good reading and proposed to this end the Book of Job. This we undertook with Wheeler as reader and I as listener and commentator. In the course of a few months, by reading some chapters each week, we completed the book to our great edification. To natural historians with a psychological trend this book of the Old Testament is a marvelously intimate portrayal of an abnormal personality who is forced to consider some of the most difficult problems of the human soul, the place and meaning of pain and affliction in this life of man. We read Job and pondered it with a deep sense of its significance. When we were in the midst of its perusal Wheeler burst out with the ejaculation, "This organization is the Sunday School." And from that day until this these meetings have been so called. Its growth was gradual and for a number of years its membership did not pass beyond the two founding associates. To this number in the course of time we added a third, Dr. Leigh Hoadley, and after the lamented death of Wheeler a fourth, Dr. Alfred S. Romer. Thus it remains today and with its original purpose, perhaps its chief one, an escape from the over-pressure of American, and particularly Harvard University life.

The Sunday School, though an organization of very limited membership, has always been generous toward guests. It invites at present to the Amalfi, for the Capri, as already mentioned, has vanished. At the Amalfi we sit in a corner compartment that accommodates four freely, six or even seven on pressure. One of the corner places is reserved for our special guest, if such there be, and in this corner we have entertained a number of scientific notables, even Nobel prize-winners. Among these were A. V. Hill of London; Hans Spemann, of Freiburg im Breisgau; O. Loewi, formerly of Graz, Austria; E. D. Adrian, of Cambridge, England; T. Svedberg, of Uppsala, Sweden; and A. Szent Györgi, formerly of Szeged, Hungary. Here, too, many other distinguished scientific guests have honored us with their presence. When Professor James Gray, now head of the zoological laboratory at Cambridge University, England, was in this country, he broke bread with us and having discovered that there was a legitimate way of having Italian home-made wine even in the days of prohibition in the United States, he was so impressed with the situation as to declare that on his return to England he would write an article on the progress of the Sunday School movement in America. Thus the undue pressure of American academic life has been in some degree alleviated by this simple and unconventional organization.

Another form of relaxation which has been a lifelong pleasure to me is walking. My family was one of good walkers and my father early instilled in me a liking for this healthful and enjoyable exercise. It was one of my great delights as a growing lad to be taken by my father on Saturday or Sunday afternoons to walk in the country, or more frequently in Fairmount Park near which we lived. The park extended some four to five miles on both sides of the Schuylkill and gave us ample space for a full half day's tramp. When I came to Harvard I found in Dr. Walter Faxon, already mentioned in this volume, a most congenial guide to what was of interest to a pedestrian about Cambridge. Dr. Faxon took me to Lexington and to Concord, where I saw for the first time much that concerned the revolutionary and literary history of our country. He introduced me to the Blue Hills with their beautiful scenery and extended prospects, to Nahant and to Marblehead with their rugged shorelines, and to Salem with its witch traditions and its associations with Hawthorne. Here Dr. Faxon introduced me to Mr. John Robinson, an old friend of his, and a direct descendant of that John Robinson who, as the Puritan minister of his day, had come from Holland to take part in the settlement of Salem in the new world. Thus through our walks Dr. Faxon made me familiar with the New England countryside and its historic traditions.

Nor have such walks lost their charm for me even in my full maturity.

In the early days of my married life the vogue of the bicycle was at its height and my wife and I both were given to riding the wheel, but this did not replace our pleasure in walking which could carry us to many places not accessible otherwise. This was particularly true of the New England mountains. When, for the improvement of my health, we spent a summer in Jaffrey, New Hampshire, at the base of Mount Monadnock, we could indulge without limit in walks and climbs on the sides of this friendly peak. At the time of our first visit to Monadnock in 1897 there was no clear trail up the mountain from the Jaffrey side. With the help of Mr. Arthur E. Poole, the son of the farmer and his wife who maintained the farmhouse, the Ark, at which we stayed, we projected a trail up the Jaffrey side of the mountain, following in general the course of a beautiful mountain stream, Meade's Brook, and eventually leading to the summit. In the course of several summers this trail was completed, marked by some five hundred and more red crosses, and eventually became a much frequented way to the top of the mountain. Although we designated it the Ark Trail it was always known as the Red Cross Trail, and as such survived a goodly number of years after which it was condemned and closed, for the brook near it was taken over as a part of the Jaffrey public water-supply. This early work on Monadnock confirmed my wife and myself in mountain tramping and climbing, and from 1897 to the present time we have enjoyed this form of exercise. It has added greatly to our pleasure at many places, particularly in the Canadian Rockies and in our own West Coast.

In the early part of the nineteen-hundreds several of us in Cambridge were given to Sunday walks. The nucleus of this body was Dr. Winthrop Osterhout, already mentioned, Mr. Frederick Rogers, a Yale graduate who had married an intimate friend of ours, Sidney Wilkins, and myself. We three with usually a dozen or more young people and some of their elders commonly walked in good weather into the countryside in the immediate neighborhood of Cambridge. We sought out such objectives as Prospect Hill in Waltham, Arlington Heights to the northwest of Cambridge, or the observatories in the Middlesex Fells, and even in snow or rain we came thus to know in an intimate way many of the charming spots about our residential town. This led to walking trips of much greater extent, taken by several of our more mature members and carried out in the early autumn while the weather was still pleasant. Two of these, one to Mount Marcy in the Adirondacks and the other to the Presidential Range and Mount Washington, were especially enjoyable.

The party to Mount Marcy gathered at Westport on Lake Champlain and consisted of four persons: Dr. E. G. Conklin of Princeton University, Mr. F. W. Rogers, my colleague Dr. W. M. Wheeler, and myself. From Westport we had an easy walk to Elizabethtown where we stopped overnight, and the next day we made our way to St. Hubert's Inn. This we discovered on our arrival was no longer a public inn but had been changed into something like a country club with a limited membership. The manager told us with regret that only members and their guests could be put up. When the manager learned a little more about us and our intentions to climb Mount Marcy he suggested that we might have a friend on their membership list who, if then at the Inn, might introduce us as his guests and thus enable us to stay overnight. We scanned the list of those at the Inn and by good fortune Conklin discovered a Philadelphian whom he knew and who might take us under his protection. He was found, greeted Conklin most cordially, and willingly sponsored us all. The manager then gladly entered us as guests and when he heard our desires in general advised us strongly to obtain a guide at once and make our way that afternoon to one of the camps on upper Ausable Lake where we could stay overnight, and then make an early morning start for Mount Marcy. To find a guide was not easy, for it was their busy season, but eventually we discovered one, Ed by name, who agreed to start us on our way so that we could reach the summit of Marcy by noon, any trail on the other side would lead us into Placid, for all went to one destination and all were freely open and clearly marked. Ed agreed to collect provisions and other necessities and in the late afternoon we bade our good friends at the Inn good-bye and with ample packs started out for the lower Ausable. Here we found canoes and paddled to its upper end. Then after a short overland carry we came to the upper Ausable over which we again paddled to an ample camp where we were to stay for the night. Ed cooked supper for us and we slept on beds of balsam fir. We were up by six the next morning, had a quick breakfast, and, while we cleaned up the camp, Ed prepared our midday meal and put it in a special pack. We left the camp about seven and took a direct course which according to Ed was the best way up that side of Marcy. It was hard going through timber much of which had fallen. Finally about ten we came out on the more open mountain slope and began a steady ascent. We reached the head of a valley which Ed told us led into Keene and here he said he must leave us to meet a second party that he had agreed to guide that evening. The summit of Marcy was within easy sight and we said good-bye to our guide who disappeared very quickly leaving his pack of provisions with us and full directions for the summit. We pressed on valiantly and reached the top of Marcy about noon. And what a view we had! The Adirondacks spread out in all directions at our feet! The day as clear as anyone could wish. We saw, well marked, the beginning of the trail down to Placid. Having taken in all these matters we fell to our pack of midday lunch. And now we learned what a deceiver Ed had been. Three thin sandwiches for four hungry men and all the rest of the pack filled with paper, empty receptacles and the like! We shook our fists toward Keene and hoped that our mittened imprecations reached Ed on his descent. Why we had been given such scurvy treatment we never learned. We suspected that Ed had been forced by the Inn management to take us on when he wished to rest from guiding, but we never really learned the reason for our ill treatment. Up over five thousand feet on Marcy and with no real food short of its base we looked about the summit with eyes of revenge. We shared our meagre supply of buttered bread very evenly and a little before one o'clock began our long, long trek toward Placid. The trail though clear was none too easy, and weak from insufficient food we stumbled on in silence. We walked all the afternoon and into the evening. At last we gained a narrow road and where it crossed a small stream Wheeler stopped, took off his shoes, and bathed his swollen feet. Then, after half an hour's rest, on again we went into the darkening night. It seemed as though we were doomed to put up supperless overnight somewhere on the open road. At last Rogers, who was ahead, descried a distant light. We pressed eagerly on and finally reached a farmhouse between nine and ten in the evening. The light shone from the kitchen where the good woman of the place was finishing her chores. She looked on us with no welcoming eyes, told us her home was filled with boarders, that she could give us nothing to eat and when we pleaded for places in the barn she said that it was fully occupied by her family. When, however, she heard our pathetic tale of hunger she relented and gave us a great bowl of warm, mashed Irish potatoes and boiled us a dozen eggs. We ate every scrap she would spare us and scraped her bowl clean. Evidently we consumed some of her boarders' fare for the next day, but our needs were desperate. We paid her a good price for what to us was priceless and then asked advice about sleeping. She pointed over a field to another pin-point of light and told us that it was a neighboring farmhouse and that we might find rooms there. Somewhat revived, we thanked her, picked up our packs, and made such haste as we could in the direction of the light. We were just in time, for it was now quite late and the house was being closed for the night. We explained how we had learned of the place and when we told the woman in charge that we wanted bedrooms but no food she agreed to accommodate us. Wheeler and I got a room with a double bed and the same kind of accommodation fell to Rogers and Conklin. What the other two did I do not know but Wheeler and I took off our shoes and outer clothing and in a few minutes were in deep sleep. And what a sleep it was! I never before had come so near utter exhaustion. We left word to be wakened early that we might catch a bus which passed that way to Placid. Again we paid a good bill, caught the bus, and by breakfast time we were in Placid. We learned afterwards, as I had suspected at the time, that we had slept in a tuberculosis camp. But in our dire straits such small matters counted as nothing.

After a good breakfast in Placid at a restaurant recommended to us by our driver we were much revived and were inclined to look on our ascent and particularly our descent of Marcy as a great adventure, as indeed it was. Here, however, our tramp ended abruptly, for it began to rain. We had planned that after Marcy we should climb Whiteface, but we had had our fill and with the sudden change in the weather we took transportation by bus to Westport. At Westport I was left to go east while the other three of the party went south by train. Before we parted we swore eternal friendship like four shipwrecked mariners who had starved together on a raft, but had in the end been rescued. Thus ended the eventful ascent of Marcy, but would that we could have caught Ed!

It was my wish to cross Lake Champlain and take a Boston-Maine train to Monadnock where I was to meet my wife. On inquiry at Westport I found that an improvised ferry-boat could be hired there to carry me to the east shore of Lake Champlain where at Vergennes I could make the train connections I sought. I reached the local hotel in Vergennes that afternoon and told the proprietor that I wished to stay over night and take the morning train for Monadnock. He told me to my surprise that there was no such train on the morrow for that day was Sunday. In our walking trip I had quite lost track of the days of the week and I now found myself stranded for twenty-four hours in Vergennes till a Monday train should arrive. I had made provision for some such mishap and had in my pack an unread copy of Whitman's *Leaves of Grass*. On that Sunday I read it from cover to cover, a perfect gorge of Whitmanian verse. I marked the poems that pleased me most and this copy has been a joy among my books ever since. The Monday train carried me to Monadnock and thus ended for me the eventful climb of Mount Marcy.

The second extended autumn tramp that I shall describe was to the Presidential Range and Mount Washington. Again four of us took to the road. They were Conklin, Rogers, and myself of the former party, and a new member, Winthrop Osterhout. We assembled from various directions at Burlington, Vermont, which we left early the next morning in bright sunlight. We partly rode by trolley car and partly walked to the foot of Mount Mansfield. This we ascended from the southwest by a stiff climb over a rugged trail. We spent the night on the top at the Adams House and then after a climb over the head and chin of the great recumbent face which forms the summit of the mountain we descended into Smuggler's Notch and made our way to Stowe. Here we stopped over night at the local hotel and then took the train in the morning across Vermont and into New Hampshire. I was supposed to have charge of the weather. From the start we had had fine skies, but I predicted rain and declared it was arranged for train days. According to schedule it rained most of the time we were crossing Vermont and New Hampshire by rail. It cleared up beautifully as we reached the old Ravine House at the foot of Mount Madison of the Presidential Range. Here we again stayed over night and on the afternoon of the next day ascended the north slope of Madison calling on our theological friend, George Moore, at his cabin on this slope. We made the Madison Hut just below the summit of that mountain by late afternoon and found a small company of trampers already there. After a good supper prepared by the hut-keeper we were advised to go to a neighboring sleeping hut and arrange our bunks before dark as there were no lights in that hut. This the eight or ten of us who made up the total party did. When we returned to the main hut the keeper asked us if we were satisfactorily accommodated for the night and when we described our location we were told by him that we had invaded the women's quarters where the bunks were better and that we should return and find new places. This we declined to do for we were all men. We were warned, however, that if a late party arrived including women removal would be necessary. We listened and before long in the dark we heard a party approaching. Among its members were some with high-pitched voices, but when they entered the hut we saw to our relief that they were boys. I could not help but recall the difference between roughing it in Europe and in America in respect to sleeping quarters and how a cousin of mine, a young woman, had told me of a night she had spent on a sleeping platform in a hut on one of the Swiss passes where a row of human beings was stretched out like a row of corpses for final rest. She found herself between a Catholic priest on one side and an aged college professor on the other, and yet exhausted, tired humanity solved all social difficulties and all slept well in their clothes. As we on Mount Madison were beginning our slumbers one restless soul in the lot kept some of us awake by his uneasiness till we heard a cork removed, a series of deep gurgles, after which a toper's snoring ensued.

We woke up early to a glorious sunrise from the more or less sleet-covered summit of Madison and then after a quick breakfast we made our way over Adams and Jefferson to the real summit of all, Washington. Here we had a midday meal and started in the early afternoon for Crawford's. As we passed above Tuckerman's Ravine with its gorgeous view over endless territory Conklin who had never before known mountains quite as we were having them and who was carried away by the whole trip, climbed to a projecting rock and, looking off far to the eastward, shouted out an

ejaculation that I fear my publisher would not allow me to transcribe to this page. After we heard Conklin's explosion we all
agreed that it was a wonderful thing to have the training of a
minister before entering the ranks of the zoologist. It was the nearest I ever heard Conklin come to using strong language. We had a
long walk on the flank of Monroe and down through the woods to
Crawford's. Here we arrived in the early evening just as a shower
of rain began. This celebrated, White-mountain caravansary was a
flood of light with a clientele in stylish evening dress about to move
into dinner. We four in our tramping clothes slipped quietly to the
office and begged for some simple accommodations for the night
and an inconspicuous corner where we could be provided with
food. The hotel management had evidently met the situation before
and gave us the kind of rooms we wanted. Here we washed up, put
on as good an appearance as we could, and proceeded to the dining
room. The guests had for the most part been seated. We caught the
eye of the head waiter, a young man, and whispered to him that
we should like to be put in some hidden corner where we could eat
in quiet. He, rascal that he was, marched us in our tramping clothes
down the whole length of the main aisle of the dining hall to the
great amusement of many of the guests, some of whom we were
forced to recognize, and at last seated us in a corner to which he
might well have brought us by an almost private passage. When we
were settled he looked at Winthrop Osterhout with a wicked twinkle in his eye and addressed him by name, for he had been a former
student under Winthrop at Harvard. We survived the ordeal and
inwardly wrote it down as one of the misadventures of our trip.
The next morning, after a night of showers, we were to have gone
directly back to Boston, but the weather turned out finally to be
so beautifully clear that we took an early train to Bethlehem,
walked by Profile Lake and the Old Man of the Mountain, through
the Franconia Notch, and on to North Woodstock. We were
obliged to run for the local train which connected with the main
line for Boston. As we entered the car it began to rain and a gentle
drizzle kept up till we reached the Hub. Thus, my ordering of the
weather was perfect. We had a late dinner on the Boston express
which had left Montreal that morning. As we went on with our
meal Conklin, who had been in raptures over the whole trip, insisted on ordering wine at his own expense. This graciousness we

accepted and then when we came to settle our bills I told Conklin to be careful to see that his change was not Canadian money, for this train was noted for its remarkable money exchanges whereby the waiters made a small gain. When Conklin looked over his change he found, as he had been warned, that much of it was Canadian silver. This to the extent of well over a dollar he returned to the waiter with a request for United States change. The waiter who was fully on to his situation, bowed profoundly, backed away from Conklin with great thanks for his assumed *pourboire*, and before Conklin could recover had disappeared. We regretted that Conklin's generosity had terminated in such a mild but polite swindle, but when we got back to our places on the train and Conklin had related all the circumstances of the transaction we, including Conklin, were forced to admit with some laughing the adroitness of the colored imposter. Thus ended the White Mountain tramp, an episode in our lives long to be remembered. Walking and what goes with it is a helpful renovator for almost any kind of life, academic or otherwise.

XXIV

Personal Relations --
Researches

CUDGEL THY BRAINS NO MORE ABOUT IT.
Shakespeare

IN 1883 four of us entered the Lawrence Scientific School of Harvard University for the study of Natural History; James Ellis Humphrey, Robert Payne Bigelow, Frederick LeRoy Sargent, and George Howard Parker. As first year students we were not eligible to membership in the Harvard Natural History Society, but the following year, having attained to the standing of second year men, we were elected to that body. The society was not very active, and one of us suggested that if a college room could be obtained informal meetings of the group might be held from time to time, and an active interest among the members of the society created. President Eliot was appealed to and kindly assigned the society a room in Massachusetts Hall. Here we held weekly gatherings, arranged for the study of the natural history of the region about Cambridge, and thus gave the Society a real objective.

During one of our meetings our deliberations were interrupted by the arrival of a college officer who announced himself as Professor William James, and who told us that for a number of years past he had occupied this room for some simple demonstrations on sheep brains for his class in psychology. He further told us that this step had been taken with the consent of President Eliot. Plainly the President had forgotten his earlier assignment of the room to Professor James and, without further thought, he had reassigned the same room to the Natural History Society. We talked over the matter with Professor James and asked him if his interests and those of the Natural History Society might not be carried out in different parts of the same room. To this proposal Professor James assented, for his use of the room would require at most only a few days or a week in the year. These preliminaries having been settled, we arranged the furniture of the room so that Professor James was fully accommodated on one side, and we on the other side of the apartment. It was agreed that in consequence of our mutual understanding in this matter, it would not be necessary to disturb President Eliot by a second call, and in this way an amicable arrangement was adjusted between the Harvard Natural History Society and the psychologists.

The outcome of this whole episode was that I became well acquainted with Professor James, whom I found to be a very informal and congenial person. From conversations about the arrangement of the room in Massachusetts Hall, Professor James and I drifted into my object in coming to Harvard to study biology, and I told him that my chief interest was in the evolution of the nervous system, the steps of which I thought might be discovered in the nervous structures and responses of the lower animals. This idea, which seemed to Professor James a novel approach to a problem that was of interest to him, attracted his attention and, after I had disclosed to him some of the lines of research which it opened up, he gave it his growing approval. From time to time during my undergraduate days I had the opportunity of talking over my immature plans with Professor James, and always with increasing clarity and security; till finally, in my later college life and just before graduation, I had formulated a program which continued to mean more and more to me as a biologist whose chief interest was the steps by which the nervous activities of animals had evolved. I discussed these matters with my college associates, with my instructors, and with others interested in the general project, but I am frank to confess that of all those with whom I talked none heartened me so much or helped me to arrive at so clear an understanding of the problem as Professor James. To him, more than to anyone else, I owe a broad vision of the whole field and its ramifications. How did the simplest animal reflexes that could be called nervous arise and how, out of these primitive activities, did that enormously complex body of responses that we look on as evidence of mentality in higher creatures like ourselves originate? Such a general problem in the growth of nervous reactions seemed to me a worthy subject to be considered from the standpoint of comparative psychology, and to this

Professor James gave his most willing assent. At times after these early talks I returned to Professor James with problems that arose in parts of my general task and I always found him sympathetic and ready to discuss the intricacies of the situation.

During these early occurrences our natural history group of four was joined by a fifth, William McMichael Woodworth, who entered Harvard College for the avowed purpose of studying zoology. Woodworth was particularly interested in parasitology, and thus added to our outlook an entirely novel and worthwhile field. He had already done considerable collecting and the specimens that he brought to the rooms of the society were of no small interest. He had many outside associates and he did much to advance the society and give it good standing. He remained an active member for a much longer time than most of us. After graduation in 1886, Humphrey began teaching botany, and eventually became associate professor of this subject at Johns Hopkins University. Here he organized in 1897 an expedition to the Island of Jamaica, in the West Indies; and at San Antonio in Jamaica a number of his party including himself died of tropical fever. In 1912, a second of our group Dr. W. M. Woodworth, passed away in Cambridge. Mr. F. L. Sargent, who married my older sister Bertha in June 1905, was taken from us in 1928. Mrs. Sargent died the next year in 1929, and thus I lost my last near relative, for my mother had already passed away in 1916.

My mother, Martha Parker, was the stay of our family. She was a quiet woman of considerable reserve and of great composure, who devoted herself to the happiness of those about her. She attended to her nearest duties without flurry and without commotion. Her death has always remained a mystery to me. When her last illness overtook her she called her family physician who was one in whom she had great confidence and reliance. He had attended us all during the quarter of a century or more in which we had lived in Cambridge. He relieved my mother of her pain immediately and then explained to her the nature of her ailment and told her that she could probably have quick and permanent relief by a relatively simple operation. To this proposal she strongly objected, for she had never undergone a surgical operation and she could not bring herself to assent to one without great reluctance. Her physician failed to prevail with her and in his treatment of her case he was forced to temporize. She confessed that at her age there was little left in this life for her and that she was ready to pass to where those who had been dear to her had already gone. We talked quietly with her, but entirely in vain. Finally she turned to her doctor and begged him that when he gave her a sleeping potion to relieve her of pain he give her enough that she might not wake again. To this request he made no reply. She then turned to me and said that there was one matter in her will with which she was not satisfied, but that she supposed it was too late to change it. I then reminded her that she had left all of her small estate to my sister and to me, that we were both by her bedside, and could there take any last directions from her, to be carried out later. This seemed to her a novel proposal, but she accepted it, and there gave my sister and me some verbal suggestions which we agreed to attend to. This disposition of the matter seemed to relieve her mind greatly and, turning to her physician who stood near her bed and had heard all the family conversation, she said, "Now, doctor, with this understanding, I am fully ready to go." The doctor made no reply, but in a few minutes we all departed, leaving mother with her nurse. A few days afterward mother, when she might have been in intense pain, died quietly in her sleep. I never learned anything either from the nurse or from our family physician as to the circumstances of my mother's death, but I thought much about it, and it seemed to me that considering all that had gone on at my mother's bedside, it probably was a case of humane removal. Both my mother and her physician have passed out of this life, and we who are left probably shall never know the real occasion of her decease, but I should be greatly surprised if it were not a true instance of humane euthanasia. It has since seemed to me that for cases such as my mother's, euthanasia might well become a legalized process. With the loss of my mother in 1916, and with that of my sister Bertha in 1929, I found myself stripped entirely of near-relatives. After the death of my sister, my nearest own relatives were cousins, but on my wife's side there were nephews and nieces and their children, many of whom lived near us adding to our family life at home.

Soon after the close of the First World War we received a request to take into our immediate family two Swiss citizens, Dr. and Mrs. H. M. Bosshard. Dr. Bosshard had been appointed to a fellowship in the Harvard School of Education, but to make use of this and to establish a living place in Cambridge, the Bosshards wished to undertake with a family of that town some form of coöperative housekeeping. After considering their proposal we accepted it and the Bosshards, husband and wife, came to live with us in the autumn of 1920. At that time we were unable to obtain a good maid and Mrs. Parker and Mrs. Bosshard worked out a plan whereby they shared the duties of the household. Under these circumstances the Bosshards formed a part of our family for some two years until Dr. Bosshard received an appointment to teach at the University of North Carolina. After a college year at this institution the Bosshards motored to the Pacific Coast to see something of the United States and then in December, 1923, they returned to Europe. After a little more than two years there they came back to the United States and when my wife and I were in the orient they occupied our house. Soon thereafter Dr. Bosshard became teacher of German at Clark University, where he has remained ever since. The Bosshards, who are now American citizens, have continued to live with their two daughters in Worcester, Massachusetts, and have remained on very intimate terms with us in Cambridge.

To return, however, to an early date in my education. When I went to Europe for some two years between 1891 and 1893 as a Harvard traveling fellow the problem of the origin of the nervous system which I had discussed so ardently with Professor James in my early days at Harvard was most in my mind, and my researches and studies during that period were largely shaped by it. In Europe I worked for the most part on the structure and the function of the nervous system, with special reference to these states in the lower animals. In this way I proposed to gain as broad a view as possible of the field in which I planned investigations. Little did I think at that period that this problem would last me most of my lifetime.

From my work at Harvard and in Europe I saw the nervous system in the higher animals was divided into three clearly marked sets of organs. The first of these were the sense organs which like the eye, the ear, the organs of smell and of taste and the like were the avenues through which the outer world influenced the inner man. As these organs are not always associated with obvious sen-

sations but are regularly concerned with the reception of external
changes, they have been called of recent years receptors, a non-
committal term free from the necessary implications of sensation.
The second part of the nervous system in man and the other higher
animals is the central nervous system, the brain and the spinal cord,
for instance, to which the nervous impulses from the receptors are
conducted by the sensory and other like nerves. Here these receptor-
impulses may be appropriately transmitted to give rise to various
reflexes or other types of response in the recipient animal or may
sink into its central nervous substance as a remembered experience.
These central nervous parts may be called collectively the adjustors.
The third part of the nervous organization, often inappropriately
omitted from it, but really a portion of it, is the category of responsive organs such as we know in ourselves as the muscles, the glands,
and the cilia, organs by which we react to the receptor changes
about us. These are our effectors, so-called, by which we induce
changes in the outer world. Our customary acts are dependent upon
the unified play of all these three sets of parts, receptors, adjustors,
and effectors. We come to the breakfast table in the morning and
the sight and odor of the several kinds of food bring to our minds
the pleasure and usefulness of this nourishing material. We select
our meal, chew and swallow it and soon it becomes in part the living substance of our bodies. This last step involves our central memories and recollections and the activities of our digestive muscles
and glands. Thus, taking breakfast calls upon all three of the categories of our nervous system: receptors, adjustors, and effectors.
Whence arose these three categories of organs in the series of lower
animals? Did they all originate together or did one appear before
the others and was their union a secondary matter? All three categories are found in combination not only in all backbone animals
from man to fishes but also in the insects and crabs, in the snails
and the devil-fishes, as well as in the free-living worms, and even
in the starfishes and the sea urchins. When this problem, however,
is approached in very primitive creatures such as the jellyfishes
and the sea anemones, and especially in the sponges, the conditions
are not so obvious as in the more complex forms. The organization
nervous or otherwise of the very primitive creatures as a sample
of what occurs at their level may best be understood by dealing
with them more or less separately.

That jellyfishes and sea anemones, both of which belong to the great animal group of coelenterates, possess a certain truly nervous organization is beyond doubt. This can be well demonstrated, for instance, in the sea anemones. These animals are soft, sac-like creatures often as large as the human fist and attached firmly by a base to some fixed object such as a pile or a rock in the sea. The face opposite that which is attached usually has a centrally located mouth, bounded by slightly protruding lips and surrounded by one or more circles of tentacles by which pieces of food may be appropriated from the sea water and directed into the mouth. The single centrally located cavity within the sea anemone, and into which the mouth leads, is its stomach and serves, as the name implies, for the digestion of food. This is the only cavity in this sac-like animal and this cavity opens freely to the outside only through the mouth which serves not only as an entrance to the stomach but also as an exit for the discharge of digestive waste. Thus a sea anemone is truly a living sac, the central cavity of which is its stomach open to the exterior through the mouth, but otherwise cut off from the outside by the living wall of the animal. This wall is composed of an outer layer of living cells, the ectoderm, backed by an inner layer which bounds the stomach cavity and is called the entoderm. Wherever the wall of this sac-like creature is punctured the two living layers of this wall, the ectoderm and the entoderm, are penetrated and the digestive cavity is put into connection with the outer sea water as it is through the mouth. Such, in brief, is the simple structure of a sea anemone.

A common sea anemone can be activated on being cut by a knife or by scissors, on being prodded by a glass rod or on being only gently touched by such a rod. Upon treatment of this kind the animal contracts, discharges the sea water contained in its stomach through its mouth, and draws its living substance close together about its attached base. In this type of response the sea anemone shows evidence of possessing muscle. Only by gradually refilling itself with sea water will the sea anemone regain its originally inflated state and thus return to the condition with which it started. Does this general contraction of the sea anemone imply a system of nerves as well as of muscles? A general contraction of a whole sea anemone can be excited by gently prodding almost any part of its body, or by pressing the free tip of a tail-piece cut from the sea anemone's body so long as the opposite end of this piece is in living connection with the sea anemone's body.

Tests of this kind show that a general contraction may originate from any point on the sea anemone and spread throughout its substance, but they do not show that the transmission may not be accomplished by muscles rather than by nerves. This question must be approached from another standpoint. Many sea anemones possess, attached to the inner surface of their stomachs, long delicate filaments provided with stinging cells. These filaments can be projected through the mouth of the sea anemone and thus gain access to the outer sea water where they may be used in stinging and even killing small marine animals which after they have been taken into its stomach may serve the sea anemone as food. Each such filament is provided with two delicate bands, one of muscle and the other of nerve, by which the movements of the filament can be controlled. These filaments serve as ideal natural preparations with which to test muscular and nervous transmission.

The stinging filaments of sea anemones may be some inches in length, but those from the colonial Portuguese man-of-war or Physalia may stream out through the sea water a number of feet. Such long filaments will live many hours in sea water after they have been cut from the parent animal. If such a filament is pinned out straight on a piece of clean wood under sea water and one end of the filament is stimulated by a slight pressure a wave of contraction will be seen to start at the stimulated end and pass to the other one at about 120 mm., or roughly 5 inches a second. Is this wave a wave of muscular contraction or a nervous wave made evident by muscular response? Such a filament can be stupefied by immersion in sea water containing 25 percent magnesium sulphate and under such circumstances a wave can no longer be seen to pass over its length. If a long Physalia filament is pinned out on a board so that its middle inch is allowed to pass through a shallow dish of sea water containing magnesium sulphate and one of its active ends is then stimulated, a wave will be seen to pass from that end toward the shallow dish to disappear as such on reaching the dish. The wave will reappear, however, in the filament on the other side of the dish and proceed to its far end there to disappear finally. This test shows that the magnesium solution may block the muscular response but does not prevent an impulse from passing through the stupefied region without muscular contraction. In other words, the magnesium eliminates the muscle wave but not a transmission, the nature of which is difficult to describe except as a nervous transmission. Thus magnesium allows us to separate muscular transmission from nervous transmission and justifies the conclusion that the original wave is a muscular one dependent upon nerve for its propagation. If a still stronger solution of magnesium is used both nervous transmission and muscular contraction can be blocked. These tests can be carried out on the filaments of the sea anemone as well as on the large ones in Physalia and support the general conclusion that sea anemones, as well as other related animals, have not only muscles but control of these organs by means of simple nerves. Such nerves ramify the whole bodies of these animals and present what may be called a nerve-net whereby a stimulus applied to one spot on a given animal may spread through its whole organization in such a way as to bring about a general contraction. Such a nerve-net with its musculature has more to do with the total contraction of the animal and other such general responses than it does with local responses. It is therefore not so much a mechanism for reflexes as it is for general reactions and belongs rather to that simpler nervous background out of which a nervous organization of reflexes may evolve than to one that has already taken that step. Sea anemones have very few specialized receptors but nothing that rises to the dignity of central nervous organs. These animals may be said to possess muscles and glands as effectors, operated by a nerve-net, rather than to possess the full three categories of nervous elements shown in the higher creatures. It is only in the jellyfishes and such specialized forms that we begin to see eyes, statocysts, and other types of receptors which foreshadow the nervous states of the more differentiated creatures. Within the group of the coelenterates including the coral animals, the sea anemones, and the jellyfishes, more nervous evolution has probably taken place than in any other single animal class and yet no very high stage of nervous differentiation has been reached. It is at best only foreshadowed.

If the partly differentiated states of receptors, adjustors, and effectors is to be seen in such animals as the sea anemones and jellyfishes, what can be said of these categories of organs in still simpler creatures? This question invites further research and points to the sponges as the group of animals to be examined. Sponges are inert, massive organisms the immobility of which gives them a feature that almost separates them from other animals. A living sponge is ordinarily a massive creature whose surface is provided with thousands of inlet pores through which the sea water may enter the tubular spaces of the animal. These spaces gradually unite till they form a large exhalant passage which opens on the top of the sponge and by which the sea water taken in through the small pores is returned to its source, the outer sea. The tubular spaces of the sponge are provided with innumerable living lashes which always move the sea water from the minute, incurrent pores to the large excurrent opening. In the passage of the sea water through the canals of the sponge the thousands of small floating organisms, animals and plants, carried incidentally in the stream, may be appropriated by the walls of the canals and used for food by the living substance of the sponge. Thus the sponge, like an organic filter, gathers from the sea water as this fluid passes through its body the nourishment offered it by the sea. If living sponges are watched closely the only obvious response that they show is the opening and closing of their apertures, small and large. This operation is well seen in many of the fingered sponges, and is accomplished by a ring of muscle around the inlet or the outlet apertures of these creatures working against the elasticity of the animal's substance as a whole. These rings of muscle are well developed around the large, single, outlet aperture at the free end of a fingered sponge and faintly developed around the innumerable inlet pores on its sides. The flesh of the sponge is also abundantly permeated by strands of muscle. The opening and closing of the apertures, especially the large terminal ones, can be easily observed in the coarse, finger-sponge Stylotella of our shallow, southern waters. This sponge is found in considerable abundance in the inlets of the sea about Beaufort, North Carolina. It closes its apertures in quiet sea water, on exposure to air, on injury to neighboring parts, and in deoxygenated sea water. It opens its apertures in running, fresh sea water so that in the course of an active tide all sponge apertures are commonly fully expanded. An injury made on one finger of a sponge may induce the closure of the near apertures on that finger, but will have no effect upon those of an immediately adjacent finger. To close a terminal outlet the injury must be within about a third of an inch of the outlet itself. Hence there is no evidence of general transmission in the body of a sponge such as can be easily demonstrated in that of a sea anemone. Such slight transmission as is present in a sponge must be muscular. The sponge then, as a primitive animal, possesses muscle but no nervous tissue, and its muscle must be an independent effector, that is, open to the direct stimulation by whatever there is in the surroundings that acts upon it. If muscle is the effector, a sponge, like Stylotella, may be described as with effectors, but without adjustors and receptors. Such a condition is more primitive than that seen in the sea anemone and shows that effectors probably antedated adjustors and receptors in time of origin. These two classes of nervous organs probably arose in some association with such preëxisting effectors as muscles.

This type of evolutionary view of the origin of the nervous system then places the effector, muscle, as the ancestral organ to be followed by the more characteristically nervous components, the receptors and the adjustors. This is in strong contrast with Kleinenberg's hypothesis (1872) that nerve and muscle are descendants from a single type of cell, the neuro-muscular cell, a view which Bergh (1878) subsequently showed to be based upon inaccurate observation. It is also opposed to the belief of the Hertwigs (1878) who stated that in their opinion muscle-cells and nervous elements were simultaneously produced from the other cells in such animals as the jellyfishes and the sea anemones. The view presented in the present account is that muscle cells arose first and that around these effectors nervous elements grew up. From this standpoint the effector muscle is regarded as the initiating tissue that paved the way for the more obviously nervous elements. This view seems to have gained a certain ascendancy within recent years, for it is the only view on the origin of nervous tissue given by S. W. Ransom (1943) in his *Anatomy of the Nervous System* and by R. W. May in his recent volume (1945) *La Formation du Système Nerveux*. It agrees with the view advanced by Claus (1878) and by Chun (1880) that nerve and muscle originated independently, but unlike this opinion it declares that muscle arose first and initiated the steps for further differentiation.

Having concluded from studies of very primitive animals such as the sea anemones and sponges that the origin of nervous organs was associated with the growth of the effector, muscle, I concluded that it was reasonable to study in detail the conditions shown by other effectors. Of these organs at least seven kinds are known among animals. All creatures, without exception, possess muscles by which they move their parts and change their positions, and all animals also possess glands, organs which produce secretions, such, for instance, as our tear glands. The majority of animals are provided with cilia which in the form of microscopic, living lashes cover moist surfaces such as those of the mouth and of the throat and by their waving keep such surfaces clean. Many animals, like fireflies, for instance, possess luminous organs by which they can generate light and still others, as the chameleons, carry in their skins color cells, or chromatophores, through the activities of which they can change their tints. Many marine animals such as the jellyfishes carry, particularly on their tentacles, nettling organs by which they can sting or even kill other forms of life. Last of all a few fishes, as for instance the electric eel of South America, have powerful electric organs by which they can kill a frog or even knock down a horse. These seven kinds of effectors complete the list of those at present known, but more may be discovered. Different creatures vary greatly in the numbers of these organs that they may possess. No single animal has the full range of seven classes of effectors. In fact most animals possess only three or four sets of these organs. The torpedo or electric skate has the highest number, five, and the earthworm, the firefly, and man the lowest, three. It is interesting to note that the earthworm and man are not only limited to three sets of effectors, but to the same three, glands, cilia, and muscles. Notwithstanding the enormous complexity in man's environment these three sets of organs appear to be all that are necessary to meet his surrounding conditions successfully. In fact, when we recall the chief elements of our relations with our environment we are forced to admit that we meet these chiefly through only one set of effectors, namely, muscles. Our cilia are mainly concerned with the removal of refuse from the cavities of our bodies in that these effectors generate currents that pass from the depths of these spaces out toward the exterior and thus relieve our spaces of any accumulated waste. In this way the sinuses of the head, the lungs, and certain digestive spaces are kept free from noxious accumulations. Most glands have to do with our internal economy and are not concerned with the outer world. But tear glands may express our emotions. In none of these instances, however, do the effectors concerned approximate in importance our muscles. By means of these organs we accomplish something prodigiously more than by any of our other effectors. By muscles we produce all the varied movements of our bodies, locomotion and what man can do with his hands from digging a ditch to playing a violin or modeling a statue. Muscles too give us facial expression and all those thousands of slight and almost imperceptible motions that express inward character. Most of all, muscles give us speech from the inarticulate cry to the most finished forms of language. Muscle is the artist's tool and serves not only as his means of portraying to us his ideal worlds, but enables him on the stage to arouse in us a wealth of self-imposed emotions, none the less telling in consequence of their artificiality. These and a host of other actions we owe to muscles. They are our supreme effectors. How great the contrast between what muscles mean to us and to an earthworm.

The human physiologist has devoted so much attention to the study of muscles that in selecting an effector for special treatment it seemed wiser to take another and I therefore chose chromatophores, those color cells which are concerned with the temporary changes in tints that many animals show. The creatures that exhibit these changes belong chiefly to three groups of the higher forms: the devil-fishes among the mollusks; the crabs and shrimps among the crustaceans; and among the backbone animals the fishes, frogs, toads and lizards. When I first began the study of the color changes in animals some forty years ago I chose the so-called Florida chameleon, Anolis, to work upon. This lizard showed a remarkable change from green to black or the reverse in less than an hour, depending upon its surroundings. I was favored in this step by receiving from Dr. H. H. Donaldson, of the Wistar Institute in Philadelphia, an excellent set of notes which he had taken in the field on the color activities of this lizard. The notes did much to stimulate me in my work, and I here express my obligations to him for his aid. From this lizard I soon widened my experience to other lizards, to frogs and toads, and especially to fishes, all of which are very active chromatic animals.

In those early days it was almost universally assumed that color changes in animals were regulated by nerves. But even then discoveries were being made that led to another interpretation. As early as 1898 Corona and Moroni showed that when adrenaline, the secretion of the medulla of the adrenal gland, was injected into a frog the pigment of its melanophores became strongly concentrated whereby the animal blanched. This unique observation was soon confirmed by Lieben. Comments by Fuchs in 1914 on these two pieces of work led Redfield in 1918 to experiment with adrenaline on the chromatophores of the lizard Phrynosoma, with the result that this gland extract was found to be a potent agent in the concentration of chromatic pigment. After an exhaustive study of this subject Redfield concluded that the melanophores in this lizard were not only under the control of nerves but also under that of a humoral agent, and that both these means in this particular creature were concerned with pigment concentration, that is, with the blanching of the animal. Shortly after this, and as a result of studies by experimental embryologists, Hogben and Winton engaged actively in the experimental study of the color changes of frogs in relation to nerves and to the pituitary secretion. In their papers, which appeared in 1922 and in 1923, it was pointed out that nerves played a wholly insignificant part in the control of the frog's color changes, if, in fact they played any part at all, and that the dark phase of the frog depended upon the presence in the blood of the animal of a secretion from the pituitary gland, probably from its intermediate part. This secretion was carried from the gland in the blood to the melanophores the pigment of which was thereby induced to disperse and the frog thus to darken.

Soon after amphibian color cells had been shown to be under humoral control, crustacean chromatophores were found to be similarly influenced. In 1925 Koller was led to suspect that the blood of shrimps, rather than their nerves, influenced their color, and in 1928 Perkins, whose extended studies on nerve-cutting in shrimps had led to only negative results, made the important discovery that extracts of the eye-stalks of shrimps would blanch dark individuals but had no effect upon pale ones. Notwithstanding the validity of this conclusion the fact remained that in many fishes and reptiles chromatic changes were under direct nervous control. Many investigators at this time held that the control of color cells was not a uniform matter, but varied in different groups of animals, in some humoral and in others nervous.

A new approach to this subject was independently suggested by two workers in this field, Giersberg and Parker, one of whom was led to develop this novel view more fully than the other. According to this more recent conception the initial step in the color changes of chromatic animals is an appropriate stimulation of the eyes from which nervous impulses pass either to glands of internal secretion whose products thus excited are carried in the blood to the color cells, or these impulses pass over nerves whose terminal secretions act upon color cells and induce them to respond. From this standpoint both humoral activation and nervous activation are dependent upon secretions either from remote glands or from nearby nerve-terminals, conditions which do much to obliterate the distinction between the two kinds of activation and bring chromatic excitation in line with the modern conception of internuncial nerve transmission by chemical agents. These activating substances have been variously called neurohumors (Fredericq, Parker), transmitters (Dale), neurohormones (Huxley), or chemical mediators (Cannon and Rosenblueth). But however they have been named they partake of the same nature in that they start in one place, and are passed in a dissolved state to another where they become effective in exciting a given terminal organ. Such a doctrine may be conveniently designated neurohumoralism, and thus far a considerable number of neurohumors have been identified. In the shrimps and crabs the eye-stalks are associated with glands from which a number of these substances have been identified by Perkins, Carlson, Abramowitz, Brown, and Kleinholz. In the fishes, amphibians, and lizards no fewer than five have been identified and named. The best known of these are intermedin, acetylcholin, and adrenaline. Intermedin is produced by the pituitary gland in the base of the brain. It regularly darkens animals by inducing their color-cells to disperse their pigment. When in man its source is diseased this condition calls forth pale spots which can be seen on the hands or faces of Caucasians but especially on Negroes who when thus afflicted may exhibit themselves as spotted people. The second neurohumor is acetylcholin, also a darkening agent ordinarily produced by nerve-terminals and powerfully effective at great dilution. The third of these substances is adrenaline, a product of the adrenal glands and a strong blanching agent. Other less well-known humors, such as selachine and sympathine, have been described elsewhere. These serve to indicate that with the progress of science others may be expected. To what extent nervous activity in general may be dependent upon such humors remains to be discovered. It would not be surprising if in course of time many more such nervous agents were disclosed and identified. This aspect of nervous activity has long interested the writer of this survey who has already published a number of papers on the subject. In 1941 he was awarded by the American Philosophical Society the John F. Lewis Prize for "his work on the neurohumors as activating agents."

No one who earns his bread by work can look on his hours of labor without gaining the impression that the time put on necessary work is year by year becoming shorter. The result is that we hear more and more about education for adults and old age and of retiring allowances. Education formerly gave us a start in life. Now it is beginning to include some congenial side-occupation to be carried from youth to old age, for we must know how to employ the spare time that more and more is coming to us by this modern shortening of the hours of labor. Any person who is educated today not only has a profession, but ought to know well how to use his spare time. This applies particularly to teachers. No teacher should accept a position which after retirement does not allow him at least ten years during which he can devote himself to personal work for the advancement of his profession. A ripe scholar should always be able to contribute as the result of his experience some aid to those who are still working in his field. In this way some of our best textbooks have been produced. With the science teacher the sign of a successful worker is his research and his ability to continue this activity. Every such teacher should have that kind of interest in his subject which will lead him to keep alive a certain amount of creative productivity. It may often be difficult to discover the appropriate thing to do, but in the end such an effort has its reward, for the interest is bound to vivify any true teacher's occupation.

To any worker in the realm of science whose mind is alert nature is full of suggestions. Such a book as Benjamin Franklin's autobiography shows us how simple many of these suggestions are and how they face us day by day waiting only to be taken up. The growth of science depends upon the additions which from time to time are made by thousands of investigators whose discoveries add to the mass of scientific information already accumulated. One by one these novelties find their places in the growing structure of science, and no one can tell at what moment a real gem may appear. Gregor Mendel's discoveries of the laws governing plant and animal inheritance, made many years ago, lay fallow for nearly half a century before their real importance was grasped, but since they held a profound truth they were bound in time to reach recognition as Mendel himself declared. The gradual increase of science has often been compared to the building of a great edifice and each contribution that is offered, if it rings true, is bound to find its place. What better can a scientific man do than give as the product of his spare time some essential part in the construction of such an edifice? This would be a real return for that enthusiasm that science itself had created in him; it would be his gift to that body of information which had been for him a lifelong inspiration. Such a return in fact affords one of the delights of science. We seldom think of our own efforts at discovery as other than the pursuit of our own inclinations. For years we may have pondered a given question and then at last comes the answer. How natural it now all seems and yet how remote it once looked! The suddenness of such a discovery is one of its most inviting features. This, however, is not enough. We must declare our find and submit it to others for test. It is not fair to content ourselves with the assertion that to travel hopefully is better than to arrive, for though the search for truth in certain ways may be more precious than its possession we are by our very nature driven to seek the confirmation of those who travel the same road with us.

L'Envoi

SO MOSES THE SERVANT OF THE LORD
DIED THERE IN THE LAND OF MOAB—
BUT NO MAN KNOWETH OF HIS
SEPULCHRE UNTO THIS DAY. AND
MOSES WAS AN HUNDRED AND
TWENTY YEARS OLD WHEN HE DIED:
HIS EYE WAS NOT DIM NOR HIS
NATURAL FORCE ABATED.

The Fifth Book of Moses, commonly called Deuteronomy, 32:5.

IT is not often that an autobiographer following the example of so revered a personage as Moses can indulge in an account of his own demise. Such an account is usually left for some other hand than his to write. But with me the case is different. In *The Confidential Guide to Freshman Courses* published by the *Harvard Crimson* in September 1934, the following statement occurs: "Biology 21, which you can take without any previous preparation, is a good basic course for further work in the Department. This year it will be in charge of Professor Redfield for the first time so that only prospects can be forecast. Professor Parker made Zoology 1, as it was formerly known, one of the outstanding science courses. Since his death, the course has still been interesting, but it lacks his guiding hand. The chances are that it will regain some of its former reputation under Mr. Redfield." Plainly according to the writer of this passage I had passed away by 1934. The comments here quoted, however, called forth some remarks from my ever watchful friend and protector, Dr. Thomas Barbour, who wrote to the Harvard Dean most intimately concerned with the "Guide" in the following vein.

Today, for the first time, I found The Confidential Guide to Freshman Courses. *I wonder whether perchance you read this string of pearls, whether pearls of wisdom or those to be cast before swine, I suppose must ever remain a question. How can I exaggerate my grief and sadness since, but a few moments ago, I read on the top of the second column of page 27 of my dear friend, Professor Parker's, lamented demise. Only yesterday I thought I saw him. So did Professor Wheeler. He, indeed, went so far as to claim that he had talked with him this morning, but, after all Wheeler has retired and declares that he is mentally inept, while I, admittedly, having one foot in the grave, have felt my mind slipping for a long time. Another horrid part of it is that dear Parker thinks he is still alive and his possibly ghostly, but still apparently substantial, form flits past my door from time to time, presumably going to the library. Every time I see it now I hastily avert my face and repeat a brief prayer that my reason may still be spared for a few short months.*

R. I. P.

Chronological Record

GEORGE HOWARD PARKER

1864, Dec. 23.	Born in Philadelphia, Pa.
1874, Sept.	Entered Friends' Central School, Philadelphia.
1880, Nov.	Jessup Fellow, Philadelphia Academy of Natural Science.
1883, Sept.	Entered Lawrence Scientific School, Harvard University.
1887, June.	S.B. Harvard.
1888, Sept.	Instructor in Zoology, Harvard.
1891, June.	S.D. Harvard. European Fellowship, two years.
1893, Sept.	Instructor in Zoology, Harvard.
1894, June 15.	Married Louise Merritt Stabler, Brooklyn, N. Y.
1895.	Fellow American Academy of Arts and Sciences, Boston.
1899, Sept.	Assistant Professor of Zoology, Harvard.
1906, Sept.	Professor of Zoology, Harvard.
1911.	Member American Philosophical Society, Philadelphia.
1913.	Member National Academy of Science, Washington, D. C.
1914.	U. S. Investigator, Pribilof Seal Herd.
1921.	Exchange professor to the western colleges.
1921, Sept.	Director, Harvard Zoological Laboratory.
1926–1927.	Alaska, Hawaii, Japan, Korea, China.
1935, June.	Sc.D. (hon.) Colby College.
1935, Sept.	Professor of Zoology, Emeritus, Harvard.
1941, April.	Lewis Prize, American Philosophical Society.
1943, Nov.	Elliot Medal, National Academy of Science.

Index